CONTENTS

Preface

Many teachers will have children in their classes who experience difficulty in using their hands with precision and control to play, use scissors, hold and use a pencil, hold cutlery and use construction materials. There may be several reasons for this – a lack of pre-school experience, differing rates of development, gender – or there may be a specific cause.

Getting a balance between meeting the needs of the children, whether it be to provide meaningful experiences or a differentiated programme within the demands of the educational curriculum, is frequently a challenge. For the busy teacher there is often little time to search for information, let alone put together a tailored approach for each child.

Children who need help and support in this area may require a variety of approaches to develop their fine motor skills. This may be a specific programme, a particular piece of equipment that makes the task easier, or an adjustment to the environment.

This book provides teachers and other professionals who work with children in the primary setting with a selection of easy-to-implement activities that require a few resources commonly found within the classroom. These activities can be used with a whole class or specifically tailored to meet individual needs. There is a trouble-shooting section which considers specific fine motor problem areas frequently encountered in the classroom and a range of strategies to try. It also offers background information on the anatomy of the hand, the components of fine motor skills and fine motor development, and a useful checklist to aid target-setting.

The book will be a valuable resource for classroom teachers, SENCos and learning support assistants, as well as occupational therapists and technicians.

Introduction

The work of children is play. Through play a child learns about his environment and how to interact with it. Watch those children at play, pushing, poking, grabbing then letting go, using tools to pour and make marks, the whole time exploring, discovering, repeating, and continually adapting to the task. He learns to talk by learning the name of the object he holds in his hand, and describing the activity he is engaged in.

Our hands allow us a primary means of interacting with the physical environment, both through the dexterous grasp and manipulation of objects and as the enabler of multiple tool functions. The enormous variety of actions accomplished by our hand ranges from the practical to the creative.

A. Henderson and C. Pehoski, Hand Function in the Child, *1995*

The hand is made up of numerous and complex structures. It is an intricate piece of engineering that has the ability not only to sense but also to act at the same time. Erhardt (1999; see **References**, p. 27) points out that hands can adjust themselves to the hardest as well as the most sensitive work. Our hands are our tools; they allow us to interact with the world around us in play, work and self-care. When our hands are free from problems, it is easy to take them for granted.

In the introductory chapter we consider those children in our classes who find it difficult to use their hands in everyday tasks. We look at the types of problems they might experience and at some practical strategies that may help.

What are fine motor skills?

Fine motor skills allow delicate manipulation of objects. They may be defined as the skills dependent on ability to co-ordinate the action of the eyes and hands in performing precise manipulative movements (eye–hand co-ordination). The development of these skills takes place after most of the gross motor skills have been mastered.

Most activities that we undertake require the use of two hands working together. These are referred to as bi-manual skills. We do some things that require the use of only one hand; these are referred to as uni-manual activities – for example, opening a door. There is a third type of manipulative skill, graphic activity, which includes drawing and handwriting. In general, children show the most improvement in simple fine motor control from 4 to 6 years, whereas more complex control tends to improve gradually from 5 to 12 years. Isolated finger, hand and wrist movements tend to improve significantly between 5 and 8 years.

Vision plays an important role in the acquisition and mastery of fine motor control; visual experiences provide the feedback necessary for us to make adjustments for accurate movements with our hands.

A further essential aspect of the development and refinement of fine motor actions is kinaesthesia (movement sense). It is gained by the input from receptors in the muscles, joints, tendons and skin. Of course, without the unique mechanical structure of the hand it would be impossible to do the everyday things we all take for granted.

The chapter that follows begins to look in more detail at the components necessary for using our hands for work and play.

Sensory and Mechanical Components of Hand Function

Anatomy – handy facts

The human hand distinguishes us from other mammals and primates. It is made up of twenty-seven bones. The wrist accounts for eight, the palm contains five and the remaining fourteen are in the fingers and thumb.

The wrist: These bones are arranged in two rows of four and fit into a shallow socket formed by the bones of the forearm.

The palm: The five bones are for each of the digits (fingers and thumb). The palm is structured with three 'arches' that provide a balance between being able to stabilise the joints and at the same time allow them to move. One arch may be seen when holding objects in the thumb and index finger: a 'ring' shape is formed by the fingers. The second occurs when the fingers are more isolated and separated, for example when we fold down the ring and little fingers to hold scissors with the index and middle fingers and thumb; and the third when we form a three-fingered (tripod) pencil grasp or pick up coins.

The fingers and thumb: There are two bones in the thumb and three in each of the fingers. Each finger is divided by joints which act as hinges. The thumb has the significant ability of opposing the fingers. **Finger and thumb opposition** is essential for precise grips to be made.

The joints of the hand, fingers and thumb are covered on the ends with white, shiny cartilage material that has a rubbery texture. Its function is to absorb shock and provide an extremely smooth surface for the joints to move over.

Muscles and tendons: Many of the muscles that control the hand start at the elbow or forearm. Some control the bending or straightening of the wrist. Others influence the motion of the fingers and thumb. Many of these muscles help position and hold the wrist and hand while the thumb and fingers grip or perform fine motor actions. They also provide the hand with strength.

The structure of the hand allows us to do many complex things. If you injure a part of your hand, even just by getting a splinter in a finger, you become more aware of how the hand feels and moves and realise that you need to make some adjustments for previously unconscious actions.

A sense of touch

Nerves: All the nerves that travel to the hand and fingers and thumb begin together at the shoulder. They carry signals from the brain to the muscles that move the arm, hand, fingers and thumb. The nerves also carry signals back to the brain about **sensations** such as touch, pain (including itch and tickle) and temperature (hot or cold).

Senses: The bones and joints and the muscles in the hands not only work together, but with the skin they contribute to telling us about the position and movement of our hands and arms without our needing to look. This information helps in making spatial and temporal (time) adjustments for fine motor tasks. It also enables us to control movement by making subtle variations in strength, force and pressure.

Touch: Our touch or tactile system is one of the human senses. It not only provides us with sensations but also gives rise to various feelings – for instance a tender touch, signalling warmth and love.

The tactile system has two main aspects:
• **Protective system** – This is responsible for the body automatically withdrawing or defending itself from touch that is interpreted as harmful.

• **Discriminative system** – This provides the brain with information regarding the size, shape and texture of objects in our environment (Bissell *et al*. 1998).

Some children are very sensitive to textures and may be distressed by them. Negative behaviours such as crying and tantrums may be exhibited, and some children vomit or use avoidance strategies – all of which have the potential to be misinterpreted. Some children are oversensitive; others are undersensitive; they may feel as if they do everything with rubber gloves on. They find it hard to judge force or pressure when manipulating toys or tools, and may break things without meaning to or press too hard when colouring in.

Motor planning

Motor planning is the ability to organise, plan and execute new or unpractised motor tasks. It is the first step to learning new skills, involving knowing where to start, what to do next and how to correct the action if it goes wrong. In order to plan movements, the brain requires information from sensations from the eyes, ears, skin, muscle and joints, and from movement and gravity receptors. Practice is needed for a skill to become automatic. The classroom challenges a child's planning skills. Some never seem to be able to remember how to set about a relatively simple task. They may master it one day but have apparently lost it on the next occasion. To an observer it may seem that the child is not responding to instructions. Often it is not that they haven't been listening, but that one instruction follows another so quickly that their body cannot respond soon enough. Each single instruction for them is a series of actions (Levine 1991).

Reflexes

Being able to use our hands under our own control requires the integration of what are known as the baby reflexes, such as the grasp reflex (automatic closure of the fingers around an object when pressure and tactile input is applied to the palm). Voluntary grasp develops at between 4 and 6 months of age. The infant begins to use visual information to help their hands get ready to hold an object by opening the fingers and shaping the hand according to its size and shape (Corbetta and Mounound 1990).

Another baby reflex occurs when the baby, lying on their back, is looking towards their arm, which is extended away from them. As they bring the hand to their mouth, their head turns the other way, so they never get their hand to their mouth. This reflex is usually integrated by 6 months of age.

Getting to grips

The muscles also provide strength so we can use our fingers for all sorts of actions, such as doing up buttons, holding a pencil and holding a beaker while drinking from it.

Below are some of the grips and grasps that we use for different tasks. The table on pages 13–15 shows when these develop.

Power grasps

- Cylindrical grasp (fist grasp)

- Spherical grasp

- Hook grip

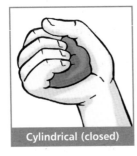 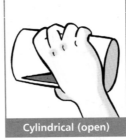 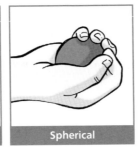 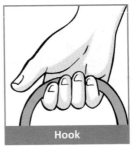

| Cylindrical (closed) | Cylindrical (open) | Spherical | Hook |

Precision grasps

- Pad to pad includes the **chuck** grip and **tripod** grips

- Tip to tip – **pincer** grip

- **Key** grip (side of index finger and thumb)

 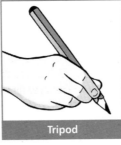 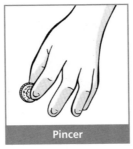 

| Chuck | Tripod | Pincer | Key |

Letting go

By 5 to 6 months of age a child begins to show an ability to let go of objects. However, they do not have total command of this skill until they have gained greater control over straightening the fingers. The development of **release** can be seen when the child begins to transfer an object from one hand to the other and fling objects – as when dropping objects from a high chair. By 2 years of age the child has developed much more of a controlled release action, which allows them to fit puzzle pieces in a form board, place small objects in a container, turn the pages of a book and stack blocks. The skill continues to develop over the next three years, with significant increases in steadiness, precision, dexterity and speed (Henderson and Pehoski 1995).

In-hand manipulation

The arches of the hand, together with the ability to grasp and release objects, allow us to manipulate objects. Manipulation may be described as the process of adjusting the object with one hand after grasping it – that is, positioning it for use (Exner 1992). It includes actions such as picking up and using a pencil. Try picking up a pencil with the point away from you; become conscious of what is done with the fingers to orientate the pencil correctly in your hand. Consider tying laces; the laces are either stabilised or moved to keep the task fluid so that a tight bow can be made.

In-hand manipulation includes the following elements (Exner 1992):

- **Translation** – Put a coin in the palm of your hand. Now move it to your finger tips, without using your other hand to help.

- **Shift** – Make the final adjustment, for example adjusting fingers down the barrel of a pencil to be nearer the point.

- **Rotation** – Rotate the pencil in the fingers to use the eraser on the other end.

These skills are usually achieved by 7 years of age.

Using eyes and hands together

The visual system is able to co-ordinate the information received through the eyes to control, guide and direct the hands in the execution of a given task, such as reaching to pick up a cup or colouring in between lines with a crayon. Most hand movements require visual input to be carried out effectively. By developing their motor skills, infants learn to reach for objects quickly, using smoothly controlled movement. They also learn to look from one hand to an object and to follow the movements of their hands with their eyes. They need a subconscious awareness of where and how their hands and fingers are moving, as well as the ability to discriminate between the different tactile sensations.

The integration of vision and movement skills rapidly improves between the ages of 3 and 7 years. It slows down between 7 and 9 years of age, eventually maturing between 10 and 12 years old.

If you have any concerns regarding a child's visual skills, use the vision checklist on page 10 and refer the child to an appropriate professional if necessary.

Vision checklist

Name: **Date:**

VISUAL ASPECT	COMMENT
Complains when using eyes at desk	
Complains of seeing double / words blurring or jumping about	
Notably turns head as reads across page	
Loses place often during reading	
Needs finger or marker to keep place	
Displays short attention span in reading or copying	
Blinks excessively during desk tasks and/or reading, not elsewhere	
Holds book too close / face too close to desk surface	
Closes or covers one eye when reading or doing desk work	
Squints to see whiteboard image, or asks to move nearer	
Rubs eyes during or after short periods of visual activity	
Tires easily; blinks to make images on whiteboard clear	
Tilts head extremely while working at desk	
Consistently shows poor posture at all desk activities	
Uses hands to feel things when interpretation is required	
Does not use eyes to steer hand movements	
Makes errors in copying from whiteboard to paper on desk	

Using two hands together

This is referred to as **bilateral integration**, which implies the ability to use both sides of the body in a co-ordinated manner. It includes the ability of the hand and arm to reach across the middle of the body, for instance to pick up with the right hand an object that has been placed over to the left side.

As children play and develop, co-ordination of the two sides of the body becomes more refined until the hands work together, each playing its own part in an activity, to accomplish a task in an efficient and economical way. When this occurs, the preferred hand is used more consistently for the finer manipulative skills. Simultaneously the non-preferred hand develops skills in manoeuvring, positioning and stabilising objects in order to maximise the efficiency of the other hand's movements. Hand preference emerges from good bilateral integration.

Hand preference

Some people use their right hand or left hand for most activities, and others use one hand or the other depending on the activity.

Hand preference may be evident by 12 months of age, but is by no means established then and may change several times as the child develops. Handedness is usually determined during the third year, but it is quite common for a child to switch hand preferences repeatedly well into their pre-school years. For most children a preferred hand is established by around 5 to 6 years, but for some this may not occur until they are 7 or 8.

Unresolved hand preference: If there is some uncertainty about the child's hand preference, it may be helpful to complete the handedness diary (see p. 12).

To use it, observe the child in question across a range of activities. In each box note **R** or **L** for the hand used, or **B** if both are used. When the diary is complete, evaluate whether there is a pattern to the preference for certain activities. When determining an intervention strategy, consider whether the child's function is being compromised by the mixed use of hands. Remember that some people use different hands for different tasks, and bear in mind that what the child is doing may look awkward, but work for them. Changing could disable rather than enable them. Where uncertainty about the apparent preference continues, obtain comparisons by asking the child to repeat the task using the other hand. Always talk to the child about this and gain their point of view. Noting this will help you adapt any teaching and learning strategies that may be required.

Left-handedness: Our world is very right-hand orientated. This makes certain tasks difficult to do; many pieces of equipment that we use are designed for right-handers. Often this does not pose a particular problem, but it may make acquiring some skills harder for some children. Pens, rulers and scissors specifically designed for left-handers make the job easier to accomplish. See **Useful suppliers and resources** (pp. 27–28) for left-handed resources and equipment. It is important to check your own teaching style. If you are right-handed, when you are teaching a left-handed child a task such as tying shoelaces, the orientation of the movements is likely to feel unnatural for them and may cause frustration, as well as taking them longer to master.

Handedness diary

ACTIVITY	MON	TUES	WED	THURS	FRI	COMMENTS
Holding a pencil/crayon						
Holding and using scissors						
Using an eraser						
Using a ruler						
Picking up and placing small objects e.g. peg into a pegboard						
Turning pages of a book						
Opening a door						
Unscrewing a top						
Throwing a ball						
Eating snacks e.g. sandwiches/crisps						
Holding a cup/glass when drinking						
Pouring out liquids						

Development of Hand Function

When we talk about motor skills, we tend to think of gross and fine motor skills as separate entities. However, our hand function does not happen by itself. The hands are joined to the forearms and then to the upper arm, which is attached to the body at the shoulder, and hand function develops as a result of proximal to distal development – or head to toe – and from the body outwards. Strength and stability of the arms and hands evolve from the child lying on their tummy and pushing up on their arms, and from batting and swiping at objects while lying on their backs in a cot. Later on, as the child becomes more active, crawling helps to develop the shoulder, arm and wrist muscles. Pulling up on furniture and crawling up stairs add to the physical workout necessary for holding and using tools by providing good stability around the shoulder, elbow and wrist joints.

As stability develops, the child is able to differentiate one part of the arm and hand from the other – for example bending the wrist only whilst the rest of the arm is straight. This ability allows them to participate in more refined and complex tasks. For example when a child first learns to spoon-feed, they have not developed the skills to move their wrist separately from their hand, and they tip their food before it gets to their mouth. When young children are learning to write, they make the shapes using whole arm and hand movements.

Interventions to support the development of fine motor skills should incorporate gross motor skills as well. When the children are taking part in gymnastic activities, particularly using hands and feet for travel – for example pulling along the bench or bear-walking – remember that they are also working on fine motor skills.

All children are different and we have learned that the development of fine motor skills is influenced by a number of factors. They may differ in the rate at which they acquire and master some skills. The following table provides some milestones for the development of general fine motor skills. Any concern about a child's development should be discussed with their parents/carers, and relevant professional help should be sought.

Development of hand function

AGE	SKILL
1 month	Hands normally closed, but if opened grasp a finger when palm is touched
3 months	Watches movements of own hands before their face and engages in finger play; begins to clasp and unclasp hands Holds toy but cannot co-ordinate eyes and hands
6 months	Uses the whole hand to grasp and passes the toy from one hand to the other Hands competent to reach for and grasp small toys Takes everything to the mouth

AGE	SKILL
9 months	Manipulates objects with lively interest Pokes with index finger and begins to point at distant objects Grasps string between finger and thumb in a scissors fashion Picks up small objects using an immature pincer grasp (using pads of finger tips) Holds biscuit and can put hands around bottle or cup Can release toy by dropping or by pressing against a firm surface – cannot drop voluntarily
12 months	Picks up fine objects with neat pincer grasp Throws things deliberately Uses both hands freely but may show preference for one Stacks rings and drops objects into a container; rolls a ball Holds spoon but cannot feed self Plays Pat-a-Cake and waves 'Bye bye'
15 months	Removes pegs from a pegboard and can replace 1 or 2; builds a tower of 2 blocks after demonstration; plays rolling a ball Grasps a crayon using whole-hand grasp – imitates to/fro movement Holds a spoon and brings it to mouth but cannot prevent it from turning over
18 months	Picks up small objects with delicate grasp Holds pencil using the whole hand or primitive tripod grasp Turns pages of a book Takes off shoes and socks No longer takes things to the mouth
2 years	Picks up and places tiny objects with increasing skill Removes paper wrapping efficiently from sweet Holds pencil in preferred hand (usually) using three fingers – circular and to/fro scribble Puts on hat and shoes Turns door handles
3 years	Uses two hands co-operatively when constructing Threads large beads onto a lace Pencil being used with increasing control – enjoys painting with a large brush Cuts with scissors Uses large globs of paste or glue with little control Enjoys floor play with bricks, boxes, trains, dolls and prams

AGE	SKILL
4 years	Threads small beads to make necklaces
	Holds pencil with good control in adult fashion
	Draws person with head, legs, body and usually arms/fingers
	Copies letters VHTO
	Starts to trace lines, connect two dots, do simple mazes
	Better ability to stabilise items such as paper when colouring (uses stencils)
	Starts to be able to draw simple shapes such as a square and triangle
	Has ability to use force and pull
	Shows increasing skills in ball games
5 years	Grips strongly with either hand
	Threads large needles and sews real stitches
	Copies square and triangle and letters VTHOXLACUY
	Spontaneously produces pictures containing many items
	Uses knife and fork competently
	Builds constructively indoors and outdoors
	Uses tools to make things
	In construction can make recognisable products
	Able to draw recognisable pictures such as house and tree, man and dog
	In-hand manipulation skills continue to develop, child is able to rotate pencil to use eraser and back
	Able to fold paper three times as demonstrated
	Able to colour within the lines of shapes and objects
	Able to copy a cross, a circle, oblique lines, and simple drawings
	Able to draw shapes and drawings without visual cues
	Able to cut out a variety of objects, shapes, generally staying on the line
	Uses a knife to spread food; can use blunt-edged knife to cut soft foods

By the age of 6, most children have clearly advanced beyond the fine motor skill development of the pre-school child. They can draw recognisably human figures with facial features and legs connected to a distinct trunk. Five-year-olds can also cut, paste and trace shapes. They can fasten visible buttons, and many can tie bows, including shoelace bows. They can also open most packaging and operate a computer mouse with ease. Their hand preference is usually well established, and they use the preferred hand for writing and drawing.

By 12 years old, children should have mastered eye–hand co-ordination. In terms of independent living skills, they should be able to use eating utensils and other tools easily, and be able to help with household chores such as sweeping, mopping, and dusting. At school they can draw, paint and engage in making intricate models and construction, as well as using tools such as a hole-punch, stapler and needle and thread.

Children will continue to fine-tune their fine motor skills through adolescence with such activities as sports, crafts, hobbies, learning musical instruments, computer use and video games.

Skills for School

McHale and Cermak (1992) found that children in the first years of school spent 45–55 per cent of their day carrying out fine motor tasks. These are some of the fine motor skills they are expected to display in the primary setting:

- Self-help skills which include managing zips, buttons, snap fasteners; using Velcro®; putting on / taking off garments; putting on / taking off shoes and socks; managing laces; managing personal toileting; eating with utensils; pouring from a jug; opening snack packets / lunch boxes.

- Using writing or drawing instruments – pencil/pens, markers, crayons, paint brushes.

- Cutting and pasting – using scissors, glue, paste.

- Using manipulatives – stringing beads, playing with dough, putting together puzzles, sorting small objects, inserting objects into openings; using rulers, Unifix cubes and small apparatus in PE and games; controlling the mouse on the computer.

- Building and constructing – using construction equipment/materials in art, DT and science.

Supporting children with additional needs

In every class there will be some children who have difficulty with fine motor skills. For some it will be a result of their maturation, or lack of experience and practice; for some it will be a result of a specific condition. These children may include those with physical or sensory difficulties such as cerebral palsy or less visible conditions such as developmental co-ordination disorder (dyspraxia). This book is not concerned with medical conditions that may affect fine motor skills. For children with such complex needs, appropriate professionals should be contacted, such as the local children's occupational therapy service, or specific organisations who support the various conditions. Refer to **Useful organisations** (p. 28).

Case-Smith (2001) suggests that some of the most common difficulties for children with fine motor problems are a result of the inadequate isolation of movements and the ability to control movements appropriately. This is both in terms of the quality in the way they move and also of the timing – they move too fast, and let go too soon. Another of the problems seen is the lack of bilateral integration, the ability to use two hands together in a co-ordinated way. Let's consider some of the everyday things that may be an issue in the classroom.

Observing fine motor difficulties in children

Observable behaviours of children with fine motor difficulties:

- Writing; poor grasp leading to poor form and fluency, and frequent discomfort when writing.

- Difficulty controlling speed of movements, leading to excessive speed and resultant untidy work, or work not being completed due to overslow movements.

- Difficulty controlling a pencil between lines – e.g. a maze, colouring in.

- Difficulty controlling tools and apparatus – e.g. using a ruler, pouring liquids, using a computer mouse.

- Using precision grips with inaccurate release, hence problems with activities that involve placement of pieces – e.g. puzzles, pegs, maths equipment.

- Spatial relations leading to difficulties with design and copying.

- Difficulty using hands together in a co-ordinated manner for activities such as cutting-out and using a knife and fork at meal times.

- Avoiding using non-preferred hand to support paper or objects.

- Avoiding messy play activities and becoming distressed if hands get dirty.

- Tearing paper and/or breaking pencils owing to force-control difficulties.

- Difficulties with fastening – e.g. zips, buttons.

- Preference for outdoor activities (involving gross motor skills) rather than manipulative activities.

- 'Clumsiness' and frustration – e.g. spilling food, dropping objects, breaking objects.

- Frustration with and/or resistant behaviour towards manipulative and graphic tasks.

- Showing signs of quiet disinterest such as 'switching off', diverting teacher's attention, using other opt-out strategies during fine motor tasks.

- Appearing disorganised when presented with or required to participate in fine motor tasks.

- Using excessive muscular tension when performing fine motor tasks.

- Appearing to have a lack of hand strength when pulling/pushing objects apart or together.

Of course, all of the above are relative to the child's age and experience. Remember that one or two things in isolation are not likely to be indicative of a problem.

Evaluating fine motor skills

Teacher observation of children in class is often enough to raise concerns about the quality of their motor skills. More detailed baseline information about the children's abilities and difficulties is often required to determine the nature and extent of any problems being experienced. This process helps to inform the teaching and learning approach and to establish a profile for an action plan, which may include intervention and/or referral to other agencies. The better the information gained, the more effective any individual education plans (IEPs) are likely to be.

The fine motor skills checklist beginning on page 19 may be used to provide a framework for assessment, reflecting a range of fine motor skills required in the primary setting. Children become very conscientious when being assessed individually and most teachers would be hard pressed to find the time to see children one at a time. General observation whilst the children are naturally engaged in routine classroom activities (i.e. observed in different situations and contexts to arrive at a complete picture of their development and needs) is better. Some observations may need more planning than others.

Rather than a 'yes/no' response, the checklist offers descriptors. This type of recording system provides an insight into the quality of the child's achievement and the level of support they need.

When considering the fine motor abilities of children, observe not only the motor skills but also the child's behaviour during the tasks. It is often not what the child does but how they go about it that gives the clue to how best to help them. By using the descriptors, the child's abilities can be more easily assessed and positive change may be identified. Here are some tips to help you with the observations:

- Check that there are no underlying issues that may affect function – e.g. the need to wear glasses.

- Know what is expected of a child's motor development at relevant ages (see pp. 13–15).

- What happens to the child's behaviour during the tasks? – e.g. What about attention to tasks? Is behaviour used as a distraction technique? Do they resist or avoid the task? Does the child require lots of encouragement and praise? Does the child cope with success and failure?

- What is the child's motivation/attitude to the task – e.g. persistent, giving up, determined?

Fine motor skills checklist

NAME: AGE:	PREFERRED HAND: R/L/MIXED			DATE:
Abilities	Does well	Sometimes needs help	Always needs help	Comments
Can control a pencil using thumb and first two fingers near the point				
Can use non-preferred hand to stabilise paper when writing/drawing				
Can cut out simple geometric shapes with scissors, using continuous movements to cut and turn the paper				
Can insert small objects into holes, can thread beads onto a lace				
Can manipulate objects which unscrew/screw				
Can tolerate different textures in play/learning, e.g. sand, glue				
Can manipulate dough/clay to form shapes				
Uses appropriate force and pressure when manipulating objects / using a pencil				
Can pour flowing substances from one container to another with control				
Can sharpen pencils with a sharpener				
Can organise materials for a task				
Can make simple constructions, combining materials, in art and DT				
Can use tools to make things				
Can use a ruler				
Can control a computer mouse				
Can copy simple shapes and forms				
Can use a knife and fork at meal times				
Can open snack packets				
Can fasten/unfasten buttons and zips				
Other				
ACTION				

Trouble Shooting

Routine observations or the use of a more formal approach, such as using the checklist on page 19, may reveal fine motor difficulties which require intervention. The nature of the difficulty, the resources available and the views of the child will have an impact on the type and frequency of the intervention. For some children it may only be necessary to make some adaptations to the task or the environment, such as providing a more specialised pair of scissors or adjusting the working position. Others may need this, and also some fun activities to consolidate their foundation skills. Activities are featured later in the book. The table on pages 22–26 highlights some of the common problems experienced by children with fine motor skills difficulties. It offers some suggestions with regard to the possible contributing factors as well as some strategies and ideas for support.

Adapting the task and the environment

At times the pressure to improve the child's skills may overshadow the importance of making environmental adjustments. Without appropriate environmental changes the child's motivation and opportunities to become engaged may diminish. The extent and type of adaptation should be determined on an individual basis, taking the following into consideration:

- Is the adaptation necessary?

- How will it benefit the child?

- Is it age appropriate?

- Is it the least intrusive way of accomplishing the purpose?

- Does it preserve the dignity of the child?

- What does it say to other children?

- Does this adaptation generalise into the natural environment?

- Have the wishes and desires of the child been taken into consideration?

- Does this adaptation say to the child 'You are not able'?

Environmental considerations

Consider the following when making adaptations:

- Alter or change the resource/equipment being used.

- Eliminate a stage of the activity.

- Change the child's method of doing the activity – groups to pairs, for instance.

- Change the teaching method – e.g. use backward chaining, in which the last element of a task is taught first. When that has been mastered, the last but one and last component are taught, and so on until the task has been taught from the end to the beginning instead of from start to finish.

- Change the layout – e.g. change the set-up of the room or the position of the child.

- Ensure the equipment is sturdy.

- Minimise clutter.

- Prosthetise – attach additional parts for easier access, such as knobs on wooden puzzles or rulers.

- Stabilise activities – use sturdy surfaces or non-slip matting such as Dycem® (see **Useful suppliers and resources**, p. 28).

- Enlarge – for visual manipulation or fine motor manipulation.

- Allow extra time for learning and completing a task.

- The need for additional support.

- The level of difficulty or complexity of the task.

- Isolating the child.

- The need for adequate lighting.

The need for good positioning

Have you ever sat at a table and found the chair is too low or the table too high? Have you had to sit for a long time on a seat with your feet dangling in mid-air? These situations are not only very uncomfortable, leading to fidgeting and squirming on the seat, but also make it harder for us to use our hands for the task required and affect our attention and concentration.

Good seating and positioning are very important for engagement in fine motor tasks. A child's seat should allow them to sit comfortably with their feet placed firmly on the floor. The hips, knees and ankles should be at 90° angles, with the trunk (body) slightly forward. The table surface should be at about elbow height when the arms are at rest by the sides. If the child's chair is too high, leaving their feet dangling, create a makeshift footrest out of old telephone books bound together with tape to provide added stability in the sitting position. Remember that good trunk stability is necessary for well-controlled use of the arms, hands and fingers. If you observe a child struggling with fine motor activities, check out their sitting position. Remember that changing the environment could make all the difference.

The following table aims to provide some ideas for practical solutions to commonly experienced fine motor difficulties in the classroom. For a list of suppliers, see pages 27–28.

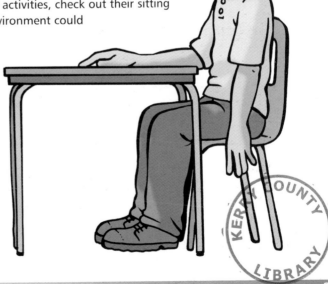

Practical solutions to common fine motor difficulties

TASK	PROBLEM MAY BE RELATED TO	POSSIBLE STRATEGIES	SUGGESTED ACTIVITIES
Holding and using scissors	Instability of joints in the arms/shoulders Difficulty separating the two sides of the hand to isolate the fingers Bilateral integration Eye–hand co-ordination Motor planning	Encourage the child to rest forearms on the table whilst cutting Explore scissors which do not require isolation of the fingers (e.g. Peta scissors – see suppliers list) Use a graded scissor programme (see suppliers list) Check vision	Play games with tongs and tweezers to practise the opening and closing aspect of using scissors Use activities in the Strength and Manipulative games sections
Awkward pencil grasp	Instability of joints in the arms/shoulders In-hand manipulative skills Underdevelopment of the hand arches	Explore a range of different pencil grips Try fatter barrelled tools with integral rubber grips Try a sloped writing surface (see suppliers list) Try the alternative pencil grip: the pencil is placed between the index and the middle fingers and supported by the thumb Check sitting position as well as paper position Try using shorter pencils/crayons – e.g. about 4–6 cm long; this helps to discourage the whole-handed grasps as there is less space to place the fingers	Use activities from the Manipulative games section and the Warm-up section
Presses too hard when writing	Instability of the upper limb Sensory feedback Concentration and effort	Try a sloped writing surface (see suppliers list) Practise using retractable pencils; when too much pressure is exerted, the point snaps Use a light-up pen which comes on when pressure is exerted (available from high street retailers) Use fatter-barrelled tools with integral rubber grip Place several sheets of carbon paper under the child's work so that they can see if they are pressing too hard Practise writing on a vertical surface Teach stretching hands and shaking hands to relieve the tension in the hand Use ICT for recording – see suppliers list for software	Use the activities from the Strength section and help the child by discussing with them what it is like when they press too hard Encourage them to make the adjustments and say how this feels Reinforce this concept in PE/games activities. Sending and receiving in ball games is particularly useful

TASK	PROBLEM MAY BE RELATED TO	POSSIBLE STRATEGIES	SUGGESTED ACTIVITIES
Lack of pressure when writing	Instability in the upper limb Hand strength Manipulative skills Sensory feedback	Stand to write whilst the paper is on the table rather than sitting Use a light-up pen which comes on when pressure is exerted (available from high street retailers) Try different markers which require less pressure to make marks Use resources that give instant results with little effort – e.g. magic painting books, magic paper (from Early Learning Centre). Use candle wax; paint over with a weak solution of paint to reveal the 'magic picture' Use other tools that will make shapes and marks, such as stampers and rollers Use ICT for recording – see suppliers list for software	Play games from the Strength and Manipulative sections Discuss with the child what it feels like when they do not press hard enough. Encourage them to make the adjustments and say how this feels
Undecided hand preference	Bilateral integration Better function in the hand that may not be the preferred hand	Allow the child to use the hand that is most comfortable/efficient for the task Provide a visual cue – e.g. watch/bracelet – to remind which hand to use	Play games from all the sections that require bilateral co-ordination
Using cutlery	Instability of the upper arm Manipulative skills Inexperience Culture	Encourage the child to extend their index fingers down the barrel of the cutlery Explore smaller/fatter-handled cutlery to suit the child's hand size Specialised cutlery (Caring Cutlery – see suppliers list) Ensure the child is sitting in a supported position	Play games from all the sections which require bilateral integration, as well as those in the Strength section
Managing buttons/ fastenings	Manipulative skills Maturity Inexperience Culture Motor planning	Use novelty key rings on zips to provide more purchase Practise on larger buttons before smaller ones Practise undoing before doing up Discuss with parent/carer ways garments may be adapted – e.g. using Velcro®, clip-on ties, sew buttons on with shirring elastic to ease manipulation Allow more time for dressing Seek advice from a children's occupational therapist	Play games from the Manipulative section Practise lots of threading activities as this is a precursor to doing up buttons. Start with large objects to thread, then move to smaller objects Play games by hiding objects in pencil cases which can be opened by different fasteners

TASK	PROBLEM MAY BE RELATED TO	POSSIBLE STRATEGIES	SUGGESTED ACTIVITIES
Copying	Vision Eye–hand co-ordination Visual perception – e.g. discrimination or visual memory Motor control Movement planning	Check vision Use colour to differentiate the shape of the form being copied Place work to be copied on a book rest on the child's desk Seek advice from a children's occupational therapist	Activities from the Eye–hand co-ordination section
Colouring-in	Instability in the upper limb Manipulative skills Eye–hand co-ordination	Check vision Provide physical boundaries so that the child can feel if they have 'hit the line' – e.g. use a glue gun to edge shapes/forms. Use glitter glue around shapes or colour within a template Use eye–hand co-ordination booster activities (pencil and paper games) from Ann Arbor and LDA – see suppliers list	Play games from the Eye–hand co-ordination section
Gluing and pasting	Instability in the upper limb Manipulative skills Oversensitive to tactile materials	Glue sticks / Sticky tape / Velcro® tabs Use smaller flexible rubber spatulas (these can be found in kitchen shops) rather than hard plastic spreaders Use larger bristle brushes with chunky handles Use fingers to spread glue if the child can tolerate the texture Continue to provide lots of practical craft and creative activities to practise this skill, as well as colouring in Encourage backwards and forwards movements when gluing and check that the non-preferred hand is supporting the material. Use visual cues – e.g. a green dot on the left side of the material and a red dot on the other – to encourage the child to see where they have to start, then finish	Play games from the Eye–hand co-ordination section Use ribbons on sticks in PE to practise the hand movements needed for gluing
Controlling pencils to work within defined spaces	Using eyes and hands together Sensory feedback to judge the correct speed of movements Motor planning Instability in the upper limb Manipulative skills Bilateral integration	Use wider lined paper Ensure the child has the right pencil to do the job Consider whether the child needs a sloped writing surface Ensure the child is sitting in a supported position – e.g. tucked in under the table Practise with mazes, with progressively narrower lines Practise maze activities on a vertical surface using big arm movements to guide the pencil	Extend ideas into PE – use a broomstick to manoeuvre a bean bag in/out of quoits or around hoops Use ribbons on sticks in PE to practise the movements needed to make shapes and patterns for writing Play games from the Eye–hand co-ordination section and the Manipulative section

TASK	PROBLEM MAY BE RELATED TO	POSSIBLE STRATEGIES	SUGGESTED ACTIVITIES
Using a mouse	Using eyes and hands together Sensory feedback to judge the correct speed of movements Motor planning	Use a different mouse – e.g. tracker ball; see suppliers list Adjust the speed of the cursor Adjust the size of the cursor Change the background colour of the screen if working in Microsoft Word	Play games from the Eye–hand co-ordination section
Anchoring and stabilising equipment	Bilateral integration Strength	Use a non-slip mat such as Dycem® (see suppliers list)	Play any of the games that require bilateral integration
Using a ruler	Using eyes and hands together	Explore different rulers – e.g. with handles (My First Ruler – see suppliers list); a variety of rulers are commercially available from stationers	
Pouring liquids	Eye–hand co-ordination Instability/strength in the upper limb	Use lightweight containers with spouts and lids Put only a small amount of fluid in the container Use non-slip matting to secure the vessel which is being poured into Use a liquid level indicator – see RNIB in suppliers list Provide opportunities to practise pouring skills; start with fluids that move slowly (i.e. yogurt), pour into vessels that have wider necks Use funnels when pouring Have plenty of kitchen towels to mop up. The child may need reassurance that it's OK if there are some spillages – they can always be wiped up	Play games from the Eye–hand co-ordinative section, Manipulative section and Strength section
Sharpen a pencil	Bilateral co-ordination Manipulative skills	Use retractable pencils Use an automatic pencil sharpener – both available from stationers	Play games from the Manipulative section

TASK	PROBLEM MAY BE RELATED TO	POSSIBLE STRATEGIES	SUGGESTED ACTIVITIES
Reluctance to participate in messy activities	Oversensitivity to tactile materials and substances	Avoid chastising the child or imposing the activity; oversensitivity to tactile input is a real fear for some children Allow the child to use tools to mix and poke in substances rather than their hands Place messy substances in Ziploc® food bags (available from supermarkets)	Play games with tactile materials but present them in a graduated manner – offer materials that are dry and do not flow (e.g. sand paper). Next try materials that are dry and flow slowly (e.g. dried pasta). Then try materials that are slightly wet but flow slowly (e.g. damp sand). Now gradually bring in wetter and faster-flowing materials
Doesn't know where to start in a task	Motor planning and sequencing Attention	Help the child identify steps needed to begin and accomplish the task Break the task into chunks Write down the steps or use pictures and check them off Minimise distractions	Play games from sections that have a motor planning component
Breaks materials or crushes them – unintentionally	Sensory feedback	Avoid chastising the child Help the child to understand how it 'feels' to press/squeeze too hard; practise with a variety of materials Offer durable materials	Play games from all sections Play dough games to help the child understand about squeezing too hard
Reluctant to participate	Difficulties with any of the above Lack of opportunities/practice Not developmentally ready	Observe the behaviour. Is it just for certain tasks? How is the child using their hands in other activities – e.g. in outdoor play? Check with the parent/carer what the child does at home Refer to an occupational therapist if concerns are expressed regarding fine motor skills Work indirectly to promote fine motor skills to develop confidence and motivation	Play games from all sections

References

Bissell, J., J. Fisher, C. Owens, and P. Polcyn (1998) *Sensory Motor Handbook*, San Antonio, TX: Therapy Skill Builders

Case-Smith, J. (2001) *Occupational Therapy for Children* (4th ed.), St Louis, MD: Harcourt

Corbetta, D. and P. Mounound (1990) 'Early Development of Grasping and Manipulation'. In C. Bard, M. Fleury and I. Hays (eds.), *Development of Eye–hand Co-ordination across the Life Span*. Columbia, SC: University of South Carolina Press

Erhardt, R. (1999) *Developmental Hand Dysfunction*, Laurel, MD: Ramsco Publishing

Exner, C.E. (1992) 'In-hand Manipulation Skills'. In J. Case-Smith and C. Pehoski (eds.), *Development of Hand Skills in the Child*. Rockville, MD: AOTA, pp. 35–45

Henderson, A. and C. Pehoski (1995) *Hand Function in the Child*, St Louis, MD: Mosby

Levine, K. Johnson (1991) *Fine Motor Dysfunction – Therapeutic Strategies in the Classroom*, San Antonio, TX: Psychological Corporation

McHale, K. and S.A. Cermak (1992) 'Fine Motor Activities in Elementary School: Preliminary Findings and Provisional Implications for Children with Fine Motor Problems', *The American Journal of Occupational Therapy*, 46, pp. 898–903

http://en.wikipedia.org/wiki/Hand

Suppliers and Organisations

Useful suppliers and resources

Ann Arbor
01668 214460
www.annarbor.co.uk
L. Jay Lev, *Eye–hand Co-ordination Boosters*
Regina G. Richards, *Classroom Visual Activities*

Anything Left Handed
0208 7703722
www.anythingleft-handed.co.uk

Back in Action
0207 9308309
www.backinaction.co.uk
Posture Pack (angled writing board)

Inclusive Technology
01457 819790
www.inclusive.co.uk

Useful suppliers and resources

LDA
0845 120 4776
www.LDAlearning.com
Dice
Easy Grip™ Pegs and Playpad Pegboard
My First Ruler
Writestart Desktop (angled writing board)
Mark and Katy Hill, *Cutting Skills*
Mark and Katy Hill, *Fine Motor Skills*

Left 'N' Write
01905 25798
www.writewell.co.uk

Nottingham Rehab Supplies
0845 120 4522
www.nrs-uk.co.uk
Caring Cutlery
Dycem® (non-slip matting)
Therapeutic Putty

Peta (UK) Ltd
01245 231118
www.peta-uk.com
Sue Mahoney and Alison Markwell,
Developing Basic Scissor Skills

Philip & Tacey
01264 332171
www.philipandtacey.co.uk
Write Angle Desk Top Writing Aid

RNIB
020 7391 2356
www.rnib.org.uk

Semerc (ICT resources)
0845 6021937
www.semerc.com

Useful organisations

BECTA
British Educational Communications and
Technology Agency
www.becta.org.uk

British Association of Occupational Therapists
College of Occupational Therapists
www.cot.co.uk

Contact a Family
Specific conditions and rare disorders
www.cafamily.org.uk

Dyscovery Centre
Specific learning difficulties including
developmental co-ordination disorder,
Asperger syndrome, ADHD and dyslexia
www.dyscovery.co.uk

Dyspraxia Foundation
www.dyspraxiafoundation.org.uk

Hemi Help
Support for children with hemiplegic-type
cerebral palsy
www.hemihelp.org.uk

Handy Activities to Promote Fine Motor Skills

Developing fine motor skills should always be meaningful and relevant to the children. If they are presented with exercises, children will view them as such and quickly become uninterested. In the light of this, the following activities are not designed to be prescriptive. They are to be used by mixing and matching the ideas to meet individual need and the demands of the curriculum. In addition to drawing upon the ideas to incorporate into IEPs, the teacher can use the activities as whole-class experiences by slotting them into the routine of teaching and learning. Some activities, for example, lend themselves to particular curriculum subjects such as technology, in which the topic may be levers and pulleys. The children can explore how their hands can be used in this way. Many of the warm-up activities can also be used as learning breaks or to prepare the children for listening after returning from outside play.

The activities

The activities have been designed primarily around the everyday resources found within a school, such as pencils, rulers, erasers, pegboards and small building blocks. There are also ideas for simple things to make, as well as templates which can be copied for use. The table on pages 30 to 34 shows the motor skills that the activities involve; you can use it to choose the most appropriate ones for your group or for individual children.

The activities have been divided into four main groups, all drawing upon the components we need to use our hands with efficiency. Obviously all motor skills are integrated and we cannot do one thing without the other, so each section considers the primary element of the skill as well as indicating other aspects. Each activity is set at a basic level, but each game offers further ideas to develop and extend the activity. By using these, one game can produce several alternatives and offer differentiation according to ability. Where applicable, ideas to make the activities easier are also given. These adaptations are indicated by the lighter symbols. The children should be encouraged to come up with their own ideas as they are great sources of inspiration and innovation.

The first section is the **warm-ups**. These games are generally designed to get the children ready. The games focus on the tactile sense, drawing the children's attention to their hands and how their hands move in preparation for action. They also help to prepare the children for listening.

The next section is **strength**. These activities are helpful for children with weak upper arm and hand strength who might have difficulty with pulling, pushing, pressing and gripping with the right force and pressure.

The third section considers **manipulation**. These activities will be helpful for children who have difficulty with gripping, grasping, isolation of finger movements and letting go of objects. They are also helpful for promoting the ability to use two hands together in a co-ordinated way.

The fourth section is **eye–hand co-ordination**. These activities will be helpful for those children who have difficulty keeping their letters on the line or in cutting along lines. They will also help those who seem to misplace objects – e.g. giving practice in placing pegs accurately in holes.

There are no hard and fast rules for using this book. Its design is flexible and the different elements can be used interchangeably. It is acknowledged that all children are different and that some days are better than others for them.

As with all things these days, a risk assessment should be carried out before carrying out any type of activity. Any issues are referred to in the relevant games.

Now let's give the children the thumbs up, have some fun and try out the games.

Aims of the games

GAME	PAGE	Bilateral integration	Differentiated movement	Eye–hand co-ordination	Finger isolation	Finger–thumb opposition	Grips and grasps	Hand preference	In-hand manipulation	Motor planning	Movement control (grading)	Muscle strength	Release	Tactile sense	Upper arm strength and stability
WARM-UPS															
Alphabet Karate	39			✓				✓		✓	✓	✓			
Animal Hands	46	✓			✓	✓								✓	
Clap, Clap, Tap	37	✓												✓	
Copy Me	44	✓			✓					✓					
Feely Trails	50				✓									✓	
Finger Hurdles	45			✓	✓										
Finger Olympics	42	✓			✓	✓						✓		✓	
Finger–thumb Touching	37				✓	✓				✓					
Hand Aerobics	40	✓			✓	✓								✓	
Hand Jiving	49	✓	✓							✓					
Limberimber Energiser	38	✓												✓	✓
Mystery Writing	47										✓			✓	
Palm Up / Palm Down	41		✓							✓					
Pass the Object	43	✓							✓					✓	
Rain Maker	35				✓	✓								✓	
Ready for Writing Rap	51														
Roly Poly	36	✓								✓					

Aims of the games

GAME	PAGE	Bilateral integration	Differentiated movement	Eye–hand co-ordination	Finger isolation	Finger–thumb opposition	Grips and grasps	Hand preference	In-hand manipulation	Motor planning	Movement control (grading)	Muscle strength	Release	Tactile sense	Upper arm strength and stability
Scissors, Paper, Stone	48				✓					✓					
The Right Digits	48				✓					✓				✓	
Windmill	41									✓	✓	✓			
STRENGTH															
Balloon Heads	59						✓					✓			
Clothes-peg Press	61		✓				✓					✓			
Dough Ball Exercises	58						✓					✓			
Finger Footie	56			✓	✓							✓			
Finger Wrestling	52						✓					✓			
Paper Scrunch	59	✓							✓			✓			
Pen Tug O' War	57						✓					✓			✓
Push Apart	62						✓					✓			
Seat Push-ups	52											✓			✓
Strong Man	60						✓				✓	✓			✓
That's Torn It!	56	✓	✓	✓			✓					✓			
Wall Push-ups	55											✓			✓
Where's The Dough?	54	✓		✓			✓					✓		✓	
Wiggly Worms	61	✓		✓					✓			✓			

Aims of the games

GAME	PAGE	Bilateral integration	Differentiated movement	Eye–hand co-ordination	Finger isolation	Finger–thumb opposition	Grips and grasps	Hand preference	In-hand manipulation	Motor planning	Movement control (grading)	Muscle strength	Release	Tactile sense	Upper arm strength and stability
Wind It Up	53	✓		✓			✓					✓			✓
MANIPULATIVE															
Animal Antics	67	✓		✓			✓		✓	✓	✓		✓		
Dice Roll	78								✓				✓		
Don't Lose Your Marbles	65			✓			✓		✓	✓					
Edible Constructions	72	✓		✓			✓			✓	✓		✓		
Get a Grip	81			✓			✓			✓	✓				
Hole in One	74	✓		✓			✓			✓	✓				
Mouse Tail	80			✓			✓		✓	✓					
Paper Clip Chain	70	✓		✓			✓			✓	✓			✓	
Party Popper Skittles	78			✓	✓							✓			
Peg Match	73	✓		✓			✓		✓	✓		✓	✓		
Peg Patterns	75	✓		✓			✓		✓	✓	✓				
Peg Tower	71			✓			✓			✓	✓	✓	✓		
Penny Roll	77			✓			✓			✓	✓				
Posting Pennies	64	✓		✓			✓				✓		✓		
Ray of Sunshine	69	✓		✓			✓		✓	✓		✓	✓		
Reel Wind	80	✓		✓			✓			✓					

Aims of the games

GAME	PAGE	Bilateral integration	Differentiated movement	Eye–hand co-ordination	Finger isolation	Finger–thumb opposition	Grips and grasps	Hand preference	In-hand manipulation	Motor planning	Movement control (grading)	Muscle strength	Release	Tactile sense	Upper arm strength and stability
Shape Connect	66	✓		✓			✓		✓	✓	✓		✓		
Spinning Top	70			✓			✓		✓			✓			
Switch It	79			✓			✓		✓	✓	✓				
Talking Hands	72	✓	✓	✓	✓					✓	✓				
Threadathon	76	✓		✓			✓		✓	✓	✓		✓		
Tiddly Wink	63			✓			✓			✓	✓	✓			
Tricky Pencils	64						✓		✓	✓					
Turning Coins	68			✓	✓		✓				✓		✓		
Twirls	75						✓		✓	✓	✓				
Twist and Turn	67	✓		✓			✓		✓	✓	✓		✓		
EYE–HAND CO-ORDINATION															
Box Clever	96			✓			✓			✓	✓				
Build a Tower	86	✓		✓			✓			✓	✓				
Catch Me if You Can	90	✓		✓			✓			✓	✓	✓			
Criss Cross Circles	82	✓		✓			✓			✓	✓				
Diagonal Dots	84	✓		✓			✓			✓	✓				
Fast Reaction	87	✓		✓						✓	✓		✓		
Flashlight Tag	91			✓											

Aims of the games

GAME	PAGE	Bilateral integration	Differentiated movement	Eye–hand co-ordination	Finger isolation	Finger–thumb opposition	Grips and grasps	Hand preference	In-hand manipulation	Motor planning	Movement control (grading)	Muscle strength	Release	Tactile sense	Upper arm strength and stability
Flip Toss	94		✓	✓			✓			✓					
Jacks	85		✓	✓			✓		✓	✓	✓		✓		
Mole in the Hole	92			✓	✓					✓					
On Target	95			✓			✓			✓	✓				
Peg Pass	83			✓			✓					✓			
Pencil Snatch	91			✓			✓			✓			✓		
Pendulum	93			✓	✓		✓			✓	✓		✓		✓
Pick-up Straws	88		✓	✓			✓			✓	✓				
Pop Up	89			✓	✓					✓	✓		✓		
Sliding Pennies	94		✓	✓						✓	✓				
Spot the Dots	84			✓	✓					✓	✓				
Trace It	88	✓		✓	✓					✓	✓			✓	

Rain Maker

This game explores the tactile sense and is a great way to prepare children for further fine motor activities.

resources

None

how to play

The storm is coming: The children sit in groups or rows. Begin with row or group 1. Demonstrate to the children and explain that, one after the other, they are to rub their hands together. They keep this movement/sound going as you move onto the next group until all the children are rubbing their hands. Without breaking the continuum of sound and movement, go back to group 1 and tell them to click their fingers (rain tapping on window pane). Keeping this going, move to the next group until all the children are clicking their fingers.

Now the rain is getting heavier: Go back to the beginning. The children now stamp their feet and slap their hands rapidly on their thighs. Work from group to group, keeping the sound and movement going until all the children are involved.

The storm quietens: Without breaking the sound and movement, work in reverse (i.e. last group is now first) until the storm has finished and all children are sitting quietly.

change the game

✋ Ask the children to devise other sounds to add to the storm by using their hands and arms – e.g. blowing into cupped hands.

✋ If some children are not able to click their fingers, substitute clapping quietly.

Roly Poly

This simple activity promotes bilateral integration and can easily be adapted to provide additional practice.

resources

None

how to play

Invite the children to place their arms across their tummies, one arm lightly resting on the other. They slowly bring the bottom arm up and over the top arm in a rolling action. Keep the motion going. At an even pace they roll the arms upwards as high as they can reach, then move back down to the floor. Repeat.

change the game

🖐 Roll forwards/backwards.

🖐 Twist around to the left and then to the right.

🖐 Alter the speed – slow, then fast.

🖐 Use verbal cues only for movement/speed – e.g. 'up', 'down', 'high' or 'low' rather than demonstrating.

🖐 They interlink fingers and roll their thumbs instead.

🖐 Let children who cannot use both hands roll one hand around the other.

Warm-up games

Clap, Clap, Tap

This game prepares children for listening and following instructions and promotes bilateral integration.

resources

None

how to play

The children sit. The leader begins by clapping (use hands to clap or tap hands on thighs). The children copy this. The leader then changes the rhythm/speed.

change the game

♥ Introduce combinations of clap/tap and choose other parts of body to clap/tap.

♥ Work in pairs and develop hand-clapping games (add more children to work in groups).

♥ Let a child become the leader.

Finger-thumb Touching

This is a great activity to develop finger isolation and finger–thumb opposition.

resources

None

how to play

Sitting and resting their forearms on a table, the children begin with their preferred hand, the thumb and index finger placed together to make a ring. They hold this for a second or two. Release the index finger and make a ring by placing the middle finger in contact with the thumb. Release the middle finger, move on to the ring finger and then to the little finger. Repeat the sequence and see if the children can speed up.

change the game

♥ Once the children have reached the little finger, see if they can reverse the sequence. Continue to see if they can keep this going to achieve several sequences of moving up and down the fingers.

♥ Repeat with the non-preferred hand.

♥ Use both hands together.

♥ Try this with eyes closed.

Limberimber Energiser

This energising game focuses children's attention on their arms and hands, promoting a sense of position and movement.

resources

None

how to play

Everyone stands. Making the same movements with both sides of the body, they do the following:

- Shrug the shoulders up and down – fast and slow.
- Move the shoulders round and round – forwards and backwards.
- Make a fist and bend both elbows, bringing the fists up to the shoulders and extending them again (repeat).
- Turn both hands facing up, make a fist and bend the wrists towards the body.
- Shake arms.
- Shake and wiggle the fingers only.

change the game

- Introduce alternative movements.
- Vary the speed of movement.
- Vary the tension – e.g. clench fists tight.
- Use concepts of left and right.
- Encourage the children to close their eyes to feel the movements and sensations.
- Use music – vary the tempo.

Alphabet Karate

Children will love drawing words in the air, karate-style, in this active game which also develops motor planning.

resources

None

how to play

Make sure that the children have space so they don't bump into one another or knock against furniture. Use karate-style movements – strong, firm, with hands out flat. Make large movements with the arms and hands (like 'chopping' movements), forming letters of the alphabet – capitals work best initially.

change the game

✋ Increase the sequence until the children can form all the letters of the alphabet in turn.

✋ Call out letters to make a simple word.

✋ Get the children to work in pairs to spell out a word to each other.

✋ Call out and make letters, and ask them to write the letter/word on a board.

✋ Try numbers and make some sums.

✋ If letter knowledge is weak for some children, begin with basic shapes.

Hand Aerobics

This finger work-out includes a range of exercises and stretches to prepare the children for further games.

resources

None

how to play

In a sitting position at a table, they begin with warm-ups – rub the palm, between fingers, on backs of hands and along the sides. Try some stretches – interlink the fingers (palms together). Keeping the hands together, stretch the arms out in front and lift them up above the head. Repeat five times. Interlink the fingers, this time with palms back to back. Keeping the hands together, lift the arms above the head. Repeat five times. Next, try the following:

- *Finger press-ups* – place the palms together with the fingers spread. Move the palms away from each other, keeping the fingers in contact. Now push them back together again. Repeat five times.

- *Palm push* – place hands together, being sure to lift the elbows so they are in a straight line with the wrists. Encourage the children to push their palms together as hard as they can, hold for a few seconds, then release the tension. Repeat five times.

- *Palm wave* – place palms together as in the palm push. Push wrists backwards and forwards and also side to side, whilst trying to keep the rest of the arms still.

change the game

- Finger press-ups – ask the children to do press-ups using individual fingers.
- Finger sit-ups – turn the palms to face up and place them on the table top. Keeping the back of the hand in contact with the surface, ask the children to bend their fingers up to touch their palms.
- Finger jogging – place the hands on the table top and drum the fingers on the surface.
- Increase the number of repetitions.
- Build up a routine and repeat to music.
- For children who find some of these activities difficult, do just one stretch and build up from this. Work within the range of movement that each child has.

Windmill

This game gets children's arms moving in preparation for more fine motor fun and builds muscle strength.

resources

None

how to play

Make sure the children don't bump into one another or against furniture. They rotate one arm, lifting it forwards, then up and behind. They repeat using the other hand, so both arms are making the same movement. Change the direction and then swing the arms forwards.

change the game

♆ Vary the speed: slow, then fast.

♆ Ask them to move their arms in alternative patterns – e.g. like front crawl swimming.

♆ Get them to move one arm forwards whilst the other is going backwards.

♆ If children cannot swing their arms, use a pendulum action. Pretend to be a clock, with movements slowly stopping because you need a new battery.

Palm Up / Palm Down

This simple warm-up game focuses attention on how the hands move and develops motor planning skills.

resources

None

how to play

The children sit at a table, with one arm positioned comfortably near to the body and the palm facing down on the table surface. Encourage them to turn over their hands so that the palms are facing up, keeping their forearms in contact with the surface. See if they can keep the rhythm going.

change the game

♆ Speed up and slow down the movements.

♆ Make the movements with the eyes closed to promote position and movement sense.

♆ Use one hand, then the other; or use both hands together.

♆ Start with one hand facing up and the other facing down.

Finger Olympics

In this game, children use their fingers to run, jump and lift weights so their fingers are truly warmed up.

resources

None

how to play

Sitting at a table, the children warm up their hands by rubbing them all over. They continue as follows:

♦ *Sprinter* – With one hand and starting near the body, use the index and middle fingers (legs) to run across the table. Once the arms are fully outstretched, try running backwards.

♦ *Triple jumper* – Position one hand as above, and co-ordinate the fingers to make a hop-scotch movement (i.e. placing one finger down and then two down together, in turn).

♦ *Weight lifter* – Place the hands flat on the table. See if the children can lift each finger individually in turn.

change the game

Ask the children to come up with some ideas of their own. Also try these:

♦ Use both hands and have a race.

♦ Use all the fingers in the race.

♦ Heavy weight lifting: see if the children can balance small items on their fingers whilst lifting them.

♦ If the children cannot lift individual fingers, allow them to lift them all.

Pass the Object

This is a great activity to promote tactile awareness and in-hand manipulation.

resources

A range of small objects for children to pass – e.g. erasers, pencil sharpeners

how to play

The children work in pairs sitting facing one another. The game may also be played standing if space is limited. Starting with their hands in front of them, child A offers child B an object which child B then transfers from one hand to the other behind their own back. Pass the object around the body five times. Child B then passes the object to child A, who repeats the task.

change the game

- Change direction on the command 'change'.
- Change direction on the instruction 'left' or 'right'. Depending on the age/abilities of the children, use other directional concepts such as 'clockwise' and 'anti-clockwise'.
- Pass objects using other methods – between the legs (forward to back and back to front). Pass over the shoulder, with the other hand reaching up behind to collect it.
- Vary the size and shape of the object.
- Play in pairs – child A is 'it' and stands with their hands behind their back. Child B places an object in child A's hands, and they then have to guess what it is before looking to check.
- If this is difficult for some children, have them sit in a line (side by side) and pass the objects down the line as quickly as they can.

Copy Me

This copying activity is ideal for working on isolated finger movements and motor planning.

resources

None

how to play

The children sit at a table and imitate hand movements and gestures, such as these:

- Thumbs up, down, halfway.
- Pointing with each finger.
- 'Bunny ears'.
- 'Salute'.
- Wave by bending the fingers.
- Make a fist, then bend the wrist up and down as if nodding.

change the game

Begin by making movements, each hand making the same ones. Develop this so one hand does something different from the other. Try these:

- Place the index finger of the right hand on the thumb of the left hand, and the index finger of the left hand on the thumb of the right hand. Repeat (Incy Wincy Spider).
- Hold out the left hand, palm up. With the right hand make 'bunny ears' (curl down the little and the ring fingers and hold them in place with the thumb) and place them on the palm of the left. Swap hands.
- Make 'bunny ears' with the right hand, opening up the two fingers. Point the index finger on the left hand and place it in between the 'ears'. Swap hands. See if the children can make ears by holding down the index and middle fingers, leaving the ring and little fingers as 'ears'.
- Increase the speed at which you make the action for the children to follow.
- Make the shapes, but don't let the children see how you have made them.
- Some children find planning movements difficult. They may need verbal and physical cues as well. Allow them time to respond to the changes in the game.

Finger Hurdles

By using the fingers of one hand to jump over the fingers of the other, children will improve their eye–hand co-ordination.

resources

None

how to play

Sitting, the children place their non-preferred hand flat on the table with the fingers spread wide. Using a pointer finger of the other hand, the children have to jump over their fingers without touching them, starting with the thumb. Once they have reached the end (over the little finger), they jump backwards. Keep the sequence going.

change the game

- See how fast the pointer finger can jump.
- Add penalties if the pointer finger misses or lands on one of the fingers.
- Repeat, using the other hand.
- Try with the eyes closed.
- Play with a partner, and jump over their fingers.
- If some children cannot jump over the fingers, ask them to jump over the whole hand, then spread the thumb only out.

Animal Hands

**Children will enjoy mimicking animal movements
with their hands in this engaging warm-up activity.**

resources

None

how to play

Ask the children, sitting at a table, to make different
animals with their hands:

🖐 *Caterpillars* – Lay the hands flat on the table surface,
starting at the edge nearest them. Keeping the fingers
in contact with the surface, bend the hand at the
knuckles so that the hand bends up. Try to keep the
forearm and wrist in contact with the surface. Stretch
the fingers out to lay the hand back flat on the
surface. Repeat so the caterpillar walks across the
table.

🖐 *Crab* – Lay the hands flat on the surface, with fingers
closed up. Keeping the fingers as straight as possible,
use an open and close action of the fingers to form
a cup shape and move the hands across the table.
Try to keep the wrist and finger tips in contact with
the surface.

🖐 *Bird* – With elbows bent, hold the hands out in front.
With palms facing down, interlink the thumbs to form
the wings of a bird. Fly the bird by lifting the hands
from the table.

change the game

See if the children can devise their own animal shapes with their hands. Try these:

🖐 *Snake* – Keep the hands flat on the table surface and slither them around.

🖐 *Rabbit* – Hold down the little and ring fingers, leaving the index and middle standing up.
Wiggle the rabbit's ears and make the hand hop.

🖐 *Crocodile* – Place the palms face down. Curl down the little and ring fingers, leaving the index,
middle fingers and thumbs extended. Open and close the fingers, forming a mouth.

🖐 Some children may find the isolation of finger movements difficult. The whole-handed
activities will be better for them in the first instance. If they have difficulty in curling down the
little and ring fingers, give them a small piece of dough to hold in them.

Mystery Writing

Children will develop their tactile awareness and arm strength in this engaging paired activity.

resources

None

how to play

In pairs, one child is A and the other is B. Child A faces away from the adult leading the activity. Child B watches the adult, who shows them on the board a shape or a letter. Child A now closes their eyes, whilst child B takes their arm (the one child A likes to write with) and makes the movement of the shape they have seen. Child A opens their eyes and re-draws the shape to see if it was correct. They swap places. If using letters, start with capitals as these are easier, then move on to lower-case letters.

change the game

- The children name the shape that was made.
- The adult increases the length of the sequence of shapes made.
- If using letters, develop into CV/CVC words.
- Make numbers.
- Rather than repeating the shape in the air, the children can write it down.
- With children who have difficulty with letter names and phonics, practise using simple shapes – e.g. straight lines – top to bottom and left to right, working across the body.

Scissors, Paper, Stone

This competitive game is ideal for motor planning, and encourages children to focus attention on their hands.

resources

None

how to play

In pairs, sitting or standing, the children face one another, hands behind their backs. Together they say '1, 2, 3', and bring one hand out in front of them, forming one of the following shapes:

🖐 *Scissors* – Index and middle fingers straight, with the ring and little finger held down by the thumb.

🖐 *Paper* – Hand held flat with palms down.

🖐 *Stone* – Make a fist.

Scissors beat paper. Paper beats stone. Stone beats scissors.

change the game

🖐 Make up new hand shapes and rules.

The Right Digits

Children will improve their maths as well as their motor skills in this fast-paced game.

resources

None

how to play

The children sit at a table. The adult calls out a number up to 10, and the children have to hold up the correct number of fingers.

change the game

🖐 Call out one number, and when they are holding up their fingers ask them to add or take away another, or divide or multiply by it.

🖐 They hold up the number of fingers required without looking – then look to see if they were correct.

🖐 Call out numbers above 10. In pairs or teams, they hold up that number of fingers.

Hand Jiving

Children will enjoy learning these dance moves and improve their bilateral integration at the same time.

resources

Rock 'n' roll style music

how to play

The children sit away from the table. Teach them the following steps. The children imitate the actions in time to the music.

- *Scissors* – Hands out in front, palms facing down. Cross palms over one another (top and bottom) in sequence.
- *Blocks* – Make a fist with both hands, place the right on top of the left, then the left on top of the right in sequence.
- *Elbow tap* – Bend the right arm up and tap the elbow with the left hand. Repeat with the left arm.
- *Hooray* – Bend the right arm up and rotate the wrist. Repeat with the left arm.
- *Clap* – To the left and to the right.

change the game

- Encourage the children to develop their own moves.
- Change the music – try a slow start, then build up.
- For some children following the sequence and making the hand shapes will be difficult. Let them enjoy the music, using more whole-body actions.

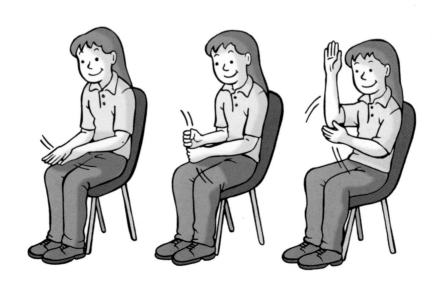

Feely Trails

This is an effective calming activity for developing the tactile sense.

resources

Pre-prepared cards (see p. 97) made from card, pipe cleaners and glue – photocopy the templates onto card, shape pipe cleaners to the images on the card and glue them in place; develop additional cards for variety.

how to play

Put the children in pairs and divide the cards between them. They must not show each other their cards. Child A closes their eyes (use a blindfold if the child is happy to wear one). Child B places one of their cards in front of child A, who traces the shape with their finger. Child B removes the card. Child A is told to open their eyes and draw the shape they felt in the air. Child B confirms if this is correct and shows the card. Swap roles and repeat.

change the game

♥ Use the non-preferred hand to feel the shapes.

♥ Increase the complexity of the shapes used.

♥ Explore different sensory materials to outline the shapes – e.g. string, seeds, pasta, sand paper.

♥ Use letter shapes – spell out simple words.

♥ Draw the shape onto paper rather than in the air.

Ready for Writing Rap

Try using this entertaining rap to mark the transition to writing activities. It reminds children of how they should sit and hold a pencil.

resources

None

how to play

The children sit at a table. Repeat the following in rap rhythm. The children join in as they pick up the words.

Are you sitting comfortably?

    1, 2, 3, 4

Are your feet flat on the floor?

    5, 6, 7, 8

Is your back up nice and straight?

    9, 10, 11, 12,

Check the way your pencil's held.

    13, 14, 15, 16

Now we're ready for some writing.

Finger Wrestling

This enjoyable game builds muscle strength and enables children to practise the pincer grip.

resources

None

how to play

The children sit in pairs. Child A makes a ring shape with their thumb and index finger. Child B links their thumb and index finger through the ring. They try to break their opponent's link by pulling/tugging. No rough play is permitted and the other hand is not allowed to help.

change the game

🖐 Use other fingers – link thumb and middle, thumb and ring, thumb and little finger.

🖐 Use the non-preferred hand.

🖐 Allow the children to rest their elbows on the table for support if necessary.

Seat Push-ups

A novel way of doing push-ups which develops stability and strength in children's wrists and arms.

resources

None

how to play

The children sit on chairs, placing their hands one under each thigh, with palms down. The elbows should be straight. They push through their arms to lift their bottom off the seat and their feet off the floor.

change the game

🖐 Lift and hold – see who can stay there the longest.

🖐 See how may push-ups can be completed in a minute.

🖐 Encourage children who find this hard to push through their arms, keeping their feet on the floor.

Wind It Up

Children can strengthen muscles in their hands and arms and improve bilateral integration through winding the string in this simple activity.

resources

1-litre plastic milk container (with handle) filled to one-third with sand (or water), sturdy cardboard tube (winder), 2 m string, sand, materials to decorate (optional) – attach the string to the middle of the cardboard tube and tie the other end securely around the handle of the container

how to play

Stretch out the string. Invite the children in turn to hold the winder (tube) horizontally in both hands, either side of where the string is attached. Using two hands together with alternating movements, the children wind in the container as fast as they can until all the string is wrapped around the winder. Discourage them from pulling the container towards them.

change the game

- Prepare more sets of equipment and have a race.
- Race against the clock.
- Explore different shapes of container.
- Increase/decrease the weight in the container.
- Use different substances in the container – explore whether they make it harder or easier to wind.
- Increase/decrease the length of the string. Explore what happens if different types are used.
- Explore other positions to play the game – e.g. in high kneeling (kneeling up tall), half-kneeling or lying on their tummy.
- Change the position in which the winder is held – e.g. vertically.

Where's the Dough?

Children will love finding coins hidden in balls of dough, developing muscle strength and practising a range of grips at the same time.

resources

Pre-prepared tennis-ball-sized pieces of dough – enough for one per child. Press some play money or other small objects into them.

how to play

Sitting at a table, the children pluck at the dough with their fingers to find the objects inside.

change the game

🖐 Add a time component.

🖐 Make the ball bigger, without necessarily adding any more objects.

🖐 Increase the number of balls to break open.

🖐 Link to the maths curriculum.

🖐 Increase the resistance of the dough used. Home-made dough or Play-Doh® is soft and easy for the muscles. To make it harder, use Plasticine®. To make it harder still, use clay. Therapeutic putty is graded by increasing resistance; see **Useful suppliers and resources** (p. 28) for details.

Wall Push-ups

Improve muscle strength and stability in the shoulders, arms and wrists through this energising activity.

resources

None

how to play

The children stand in front of a wall or a closed door at extended arms' length. Their feet should be evenly spaced, about their shoulder width apart. Keeping the body straight, they lower their top half until their nose touches the wall. Lower to a count of 5, hold for 5, push back to 5. Start with five repetitions and build up.

change the game

♥ Against a wall – the further the feet are away, the more strength is required. Place the hands about shoulder height, touch the nose on the wall, keep the back straight, push back until the arms are extended. Repeat.

♥ Press up and clap – repeat as above and between each repetition clap. Try to build up speed.

♥ One-hand press-ups – stand sideways on to the wall and press up using the right, then the left, hand. The further away from the wall, the harder it is to push.

That's Torn It!

This activity gives practice in a range of precision grips and promotes good eye–hand co-ordination.

resources

Paper (scrap paper or newspaper is ideal)

how to play

On the command 'Go' the children, sitting at a table, tear up paper into the smallest size they can.

change the game

♥ Add a time component – e.g. 1 minute.

♥ Explore different materials: try card or thicker paper. Consider such things as cotton wool balls.

♥ Make a collage out of the pieces.

♥ Roll the pieces into balls and see who can flick furthest. If it makes a mess, get the children to pick up the paper balls – good for eye–hand co-ordination, grasps and release.

♥ Tissue paper is easy: try this for children who find this game hard.

Finger Footie

Children love this lively game in which they use their fingers as footballers' legs to try to score a goal.

resources

Dough

how to play

Improvise goals on each side of a table. The children, in pairs, sit facing one another. They roll up a dough ball and use their index and middle fingers as footballers' legs, kicking the ball to score goals. Set some rules before the game starts.

change the game

♥ Use different objects as the ball. The heavier the object, the harder the muscles have to work.

♥ See if the children can use other fingers to kick the ball.

♥ Add another player, or play with two hands.

♥ If a child finds it difficult to isolate the fingers, they can flick the ball using four fingers. Make the ball bigger and lighter – e.g. using scrunched-up paper.

Pen Tug O' War

This competitive game is ideal for improving muscle strength in the fingers and hands.

resources

A pencil for each pair

how to play

Sitting opposite each other in pairs, the children each hold one end of the pencil between their thumb and index finger. On the command 'Go', they try to pull the pencil out of their opponent's hand. Only pulling is allowed. They may not use their other hand to hold on to the chair or the table.

change the game

🖐 Change fingers – try middle and thumb, ring and thumb, and little finger and thumb.

🖐 Use opposite hands.

🖐 Try the other hand.

🖐 Try a pencil in both hands.

🖐 Try other objects – paper, erasers or paper clips (short, fat, long, thin).

🖐 This may be hard for some children. Allow them to use a whole-hand grasp and a bigger object – e.g. a cardboard tube. They can stabilise their bodies and hold onto the side of their chair or the table edge if necessary.

Dough Ball Exercises

Moulding dough in particular ways develops muscle strength in children's hands.

resources

Dough

how to play

Give each child a small ball of dough no bigger than a ping-pong ball. Adjust according to the size of individual children's hands. They will need to reshape it after each activity. Try the following:

🖐 *Scissor fingers* – They place the dough ball between index and middle fingers (nearer the top than the bottom) and squeeze. They hold for a few seconds, then relax. See if the children can squash the ball with it placed between the middle and ring fingers and then the ring and little fingers.

🖐 *Squash* – Press the ball flat with the flat of the hand, using even pressure.

🖐 *Palm crush* – Squeeze the ball in the palm of the hand without using the other hand to exert pressure.

change the game

🖐 Use the other hand.

🖐 For *Squash* and *Palm crush* try both hands together.

🖐 Build up the number of repetitions.

🖐 See if the children can come up with any other ideas.

🖐 Each child can make a hand exerciser by filling an uninflated balloon with flour, tying the top securely and squishing and squashing. (See Balloon Heads on p. 59 for details.)

🖐 Increase the resistance of the dough used. Home-made dough or Play-Doh® is soft and easy for the muscles. Move to Plasticine®, and then to clay. Therapeutic putty is graded by increasing resistance; see **Useful suppliers and resources** (p. 28) for details.

Balloon Heads

Children will love creating, decorating and moulding their own balloon faces, while also improving their muscle strength.

resources

Balloons (one for each child); plain flour; water; funnel; teaspoons; marker pens – blow up the balloons, then deflate them, put the funnel into the neck of each balloon and carefully spoon in as much flour as you can, add water to make the flour pliable and tie up the balloon.

how to play

The children draw faces on the balloons and mould them into funny faces by squeezing.

change the game

🖐 Squeeze with the non-preferred hand.

🖐 Hold a balloon head in each hand and squeeze them.

🖐 Make different faces on the balloons and see what happens when they are squeezed.

🖐 Explore other materials to make balloon heads – e.g. latex gloves (check there are no allergies).

Paper Scrunch

This straightforward task strengthens muscles in the fingers and hands.

resources

5 sheets of newspaper for each child

how to play

On the command 'Go', the children scrunch up the newspaper as fast as they can to make a ball.

change the game

🖐 Use one hand only.

🖐 Use the non-preferred hand.

🖐 Increase the thickness of the paper.

🖐 Aim the paper balls into a bucket to score points.

Strong Man

Weight-lifting with a twist … promote movement control and muscle strength through these simple activities.

resources

2 x 1-litre plastic milk containers (with handles) – fill each with water about a quarter full; screw the tops on tight.

how to play

The children are weight lifters. Encourage them to keep a good posture as, with a bottle in each hand, they try these.

- *Bicep bend* – They start with their arms down by their sides, and lift the bottles by bending the elbows to bring the bottles towards the shoulders.

- *Crane I* – They hold the bottles in each hand with arms down by the sides; then lift both arms slowly in front of the body, keeping them straight, until they are level with the shoulders. They hold for a few seconds, then lower slowly. Repeat.

- *Crane II* – With bottles held down by the sides, they lift the arms slowly out to the sides until they are level with the shoulders, and then slowly lower them.

change the game

- For both Crane I and Crane II, take the arms all the way up above the head.

- Increase the weight in the container.

- Try out different substances to see whether it's harder or easier.

- Increase the repetitions.

- The heavier the container, the harder the muscles have to work. For some children begin with empty ones and slowly increase the weight. Keeping the arms straight may be hard. Allow them to bend their arms if necessary.

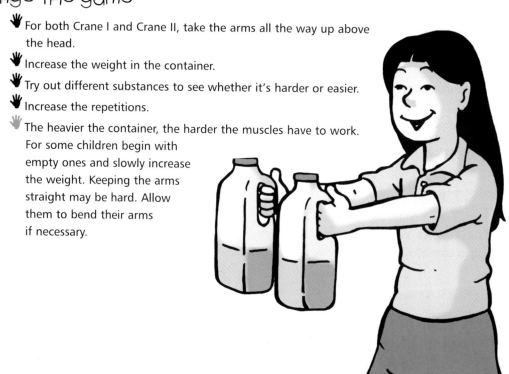

Clothes-peg Press

Children can practise the tripod, pincer or chuck grip, depending on the size of the peg used.

resources

Different-size clothes pegs

how to play

The children, sitting at a table, use a clothes peg to do finger push-ups. They use the pads of the thumb and index finger to open a clothes peg. Count the repetitions.

change the game

- Swap hands.
- Try this with a peg in each hand.
- Squeeze the peg using different fingers.
- Explore different-sized pegs.
- Explore other types of clips that can be squeezed – e.g. bulldog clips, hair clips.

Wiggly Worms

Squeezing dough to create worm shapes promotes effective in-hand manipulation and builds muscle strength.

resources

Dough (about a ping-pong ball size, depending on the size of the child's hand)

how to play

Sitting at a table, the children roll out dough to make a thin worm, then weave the worm around their fingers. Keeping their fingers straight, they squeeze the fingers together for a second or two, then carefully release the finger tension and let the worm fall. See who has the longest.

change the game

- Make the worm fatter.
- Put the worm in the fingers of both hands.
- Increase the resistance of the dough used. Home-made dough or Play-Doh® is soft and easy for the muscles. Move to Plasticine®, and then clay. Therapeutic putty is graded by increasing resistance; see **Useful suppliers and resources** (p. 28) for details.

Push Apart

This activity is a great opportunity for children to practise power grasps as well as building muscle strength and stability in their arms.

resources

None

how to play

The children sit opposite one another at a table in pairs. Child A puts their hands together (prayer position), with their forearms resting flat on the surface. Child B grasps child A by the forearms (where a watch would be worn) and tries to prise child B's hands apart. Swap over.

change the game

🖐 Change the position – place palms together as before, but this time child A rests on their elbows.

🖐 Explore other techniques – interlink fingers with palms together or cup fingers together – i.e. left-hand palm turned up with fingers bent, right-hand palm turned down with fingers bent to make a link with the left hand. Child B tries to separate child A's hands as before.

Tiddly Wink

Tiddly Wink is a good way of helping children to improve eye–hand co-ordination, motor planning and movement control.

resources

Plastic counters or flat buttons: 1 large counter ('shooter' or 'tiddle') and 4 smaller counters ('winks') per child; target (see p. 98)

how to play

Position the target in the middle of a table. Standing, the children play in pairs or small groups (or on the floor if there is a hard surface). The children place their winks in front of them in a horizontal line. Taking their shooter/tiddle between their thumb and index finger, one at a time, the children press down onto the edge of the wink. It should fly up into the air towards the target. They take turns to see if they can score a bull's-eye (50).

change the game

♛ Restrict the number of times the children can shoot the wink – e.g. get to the bull's-eye in only three goes.

♛ Use the shooter in the non-preferred hand.

♛ Use shooters in both hands.

♛ Explore how many times it takes to shoot a wink along a certain length – e.g. the length of the table, down the length of the room.

♛ Add receptacles – e.g. cups/pots – to aim the winks at.

♛ If using different-coloured winks, assign values to colours.

♛ Add penalties to the game.

♛ Play blindfold.

♛ Explore what other objects could be used.

Tricky Pencils

This game requires children to manipulate a pencil in one hand, improving their pincer grip and motor planning skills.

resources

A long pencil for each child

how to play

Place the pencils on the table. Using their preferred hand only, the children pick them up as if to write (tripod grip) near the point. They see if they can shift their pencil up to the end and back down again in their fingers without dropping it.

change the game

- Use the other hand.
- Use both hands.
- Do it with eyes closed.
- Use fatter, thinner and longer pencils.

Posting Pennies

This game involves children posting coins through a small hole to enhance their eye–hand co-ordination, movement control and release skills.

resources

For each child 10 coins (or plastic counters/buttons), a money box (or small carton with a lid and a slit cut in it to post the coins through)

how to play

Lay the coins out on the table for each child in two rows of five. The children hold their money box with their non-preferred hand. On the command 'Go' they post the money in the box with their preferred hand as fast as they can.

change the game

- Post with the non-preferred hand.
- Increase the number of coins.
- Explore different objects and different-shaped containers – e.g. try marbles in a 500 ml bottle.

Don't Lose your Marbles

This game may be played competitively to see how many marbles children can pick up in one hand without dropping any.

resources

Marbles (or similar objects)

how to play

Scatter a selection of marbles on a table. Using their preferred hand only, the children pick up the marbles one at a time, keeping them all in their hand.

change the game

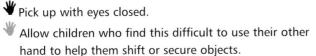 Change the size/shape of the marbles.

Ⓦ See how many the children can pick up in 30 seconds.

Ⓦ Use the other hand.

Ⓦ Pick up marbles in each hand simultaneously.

Ⓦ Allot points for different sizes/shapes of objects picked up.

Ⓦ Pick up with eyes closed.

Ⓦ Allow children who find this difficult to use their other hand to help them shift or secure objects.

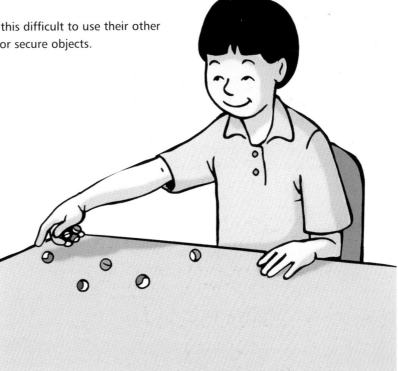

Shape Connect

Joining shapes with popper fasteners combines practice of in-hand manipulation and bilateral integration with refining the pincer and tripod grip.

resources

A set of pre-prepared shapes for each child (see p. 99) – use strong card for shapes (laminate for durability); children could cut out the shapes for scissor skills practice; hole punch; popper fasteners

how to play

Spread the shapes out on a table. The children connect their shapes by fastening them with the poppers.

change the game

❦ Join shapes to make patterns/sequences.

❦ Number the shapes to practise number bonds.

❦ Add letters or sounds to shapes to connect and make words.

❦ Explore other ways to join the shapes.

❦ See if the children can attach shapes with their eyes closed.

❦ Get them to join a number of shapes as fast as they can.

❦ Explore other ways to join the shapes – e.g. threading or sewing together.

Twist and Turn

By threading nuts onto bolts, children work on both precision and power grips, as well as developing the ability to use two hands together in a co-ordinated way.

resources

Selection of nuts and bolts

how to play

Start the game by using nuts and bolts of the same size. Remove the nuts from the bolts and scatter them all on a table. On the command 'Go', the children pick up each bolt and thread a nut on it as fast as they can.

change the game

♛ Increase the number of nuts and bolts.

♛ Vary the size of the nuts and bolts.

♛ Try using the non-preferred hand to fix the nut on the bolt.

♛ Explore other objects that screw together.

Animal Antics

Children will love creating this appealing elephant using the templates provided, and can then design their own versions.

resources

Pre-prepared elephant pieces from template (laminate for durability and punch holes), copy for each child (see p. 100); treasury tags

how to play

Using the treasury tags, the children attach the body parts for their elephant.

change the game

♛ Attach numbers or letters to the body parts with Velcro® or using sticky tabs. Ask children to count, add / take away or sequence letters to make words.

♛ Explore other animals in the same way – e.g. spiders, ladybirds, centipedes.

♛ Encourage the children to design their own creature. Explain that it should have a number of body parts (no snakes).

Turning Coins

Children practise movement control and release through picking up and turning over coins in this simple yet appealing activity.

resources

12 coins per child (real or play money)

how to play

Lay out the coins for each child in a line across a table. Invite them to turn the coins over as fast as they can, using their preferred hand only.

change the game

W Use a timer to see how fast the coins can be turned.

W Use different-sized coins.

W Increase the number of coins.

W Space the coins randomly on the table.

W Ask them to use the other hand.

W Place an equal number of coins to the left and to the right of the child. See how fast they can turn them over, using both hands at the same time.

Ray of Sunshine

Children can improve their in-hand manipulation and finger strength by creating these sunshine pictures.

resources

1 paper plate for each child (paint them yellow and decorate them if liked); yellow clothes pegs

how to play

Scatter the pegs on the surface of a table. Using their preferred hand, the children place the pegs round the rim of their plate to make the rays of sunshine.

change the game

♛ Use different sizes and types of pegs to make this harder or easier.

♛ Play with a dice to add or take away rays.

♛ See how many rays can be put on the sun in 30 seconds.

♛ Put the pegs on using the non-preferred hand.

Spinning Top

By making and using the spinner, children improve their in-hand manipulation, pincer and tripod grips.

resources

A spinner template for each child (see p. 101), sharpened pencil, materials to decorate

how to play

Invite the children to cut out and decorate their own spinner. They push a sharpened pencil through the hole – they are likely to need adult help for this. Invite the children to spin their top. See who can keep theirs upright longest.

change the game

🖐 The children make several tops each and spin as many as they can, setting them off one after the other.

🖐 Explore other shapes to spin.

🖐 Explore different lengths and diameters of pencils.

🖐 Explore different patterns.

Paper Clip Chain

Fast-paced and competitive, this game sees children try to link together more paper clips than their opponents.

resources

Paper clips

how to play

The children link as many paper clips together as they can in a minute.

change the game

🖐 Explore different-size paper clips to join.

🖐 Make sequences of different sizes of paper clip.

🖐 Use coloured paper clips and clip them together in sequence.

🖐 Try putting the clips on with the non-preferred hand.

Peg Tower

This is an ideal game for improving hand manipulation skills, developing motor control ... and having lots of fun!

resources

Clothes pegs, large piece of Plasticine®

how to play

Play in pairs or small groups, sitting at a table. Fix the Plasticine® to the table and press one of the pegs into it. The grip end should be uppermost. Divide the pegs amongst the children. In turn, each child grips one of their pegs on to make a tower. Play continues until the tower falls over.

change the game

🖐 Use different-size pegs and clips – try bulldog clips, hair grips/clips.

🖐 Use the non-preferred hand.

🖐 Use different fingers in opposition to the thumb to operate the pegs – e.g. rather than the index finger and thumb, use the thumb and middle finger, then the thumb and little finger.

🖐 Build by using colour sequences.

🖐 If using different-size pegs, alternate the sizes used.

🖐 Explore other constructions that can be made.

Talking Hands

Children will enjoy learning and using the finger-spelling alphabet to spell out simple messages to each other.

resources

Talking hands template, enlarged, or one copy per child (see p. 102)

how to play

Using the finger-spelling pictures, invite the children to make letters to spell words to each other. Initially allow them to use language as well. Encourage them to write down the letters they have made.

change the game

✋ Build the vocabulary to have a short conversation.

✋ When skills develop, work in small groups to have conversations.

✋ Explore other cultures or activities in which signs may be used.

✋ Try semaphore (good for arm strength).

✋ Try Morse code (a good pencil activity).

Edible Constructions

Marshmallow bricks and spaghetti sticks replace the usual construction materials in this innovative approach to modelling.

resources

Marshmallows, dry spaghetti

how to play

Sitting in pairs or small groups, the children make constructions by joining the marshmallows with the spaghetti – some marshmallows may get eaten on the way!

change the game

✋ Explore other things that could be used to make constructions – e.g. popcorn, bananas, apples.

✋ Thread other items, such as cereal loops, onto the spaghetti whilst building.

✋ Make fruit kebabs.

Peg Match

Children pin pegs to the matching colours on a box, thus improving hand strength and practising the pincer and tripod grips.

resources

Prepared shoe box (or similar) decorated with strips of primary colours; variety of clothes pegs in primary colours

how to play

Sit at a table. Put all the pegs in the box. Invite the children to pin the pegs onto matching colours on the box.

change the game

- Use a number dice to add on or take away.
- Use the non-preferred hand to fix the pegs.
- Fix pegs using two hands at the same time.
- See how many pegs the children can fix in 30 seconds.

Hole in One

Placing pegs on a pegboard is beneficial for children who are having difficulty with precision grips and movement control.

resources

Pegboard and 20 pegs for each child

how to play

Place the pegboard on the table in front of the child. Place the pegs to the side of the pegboard. The child begins by placing them on the side of the preferred hand. Holding the board with their non-preferred hand, they put the pegs in the board as fast as they can.

change the game

- Use the non-preferred hand to place the pegs.
- Place 10 pegs on each side of the board. As fast as they can, the children place the pegs in the board using both hands at the same time.
- Try playing with the eyes closed.
- Increase the number of pegs.
- Make peg patterns and shapes.
- See how many pegs they can place in the board in a designated time.
- If the children find small pegs too hard, try golf tees and a polystyrene block or tile to push them into. Large pegboards and pegs are available; try Easy Grip™ pegs and a Playpad Pegboard (see **Useful suppliers and resources**, p. 28).

Twirls

In-hand manipulation and movement control are important in this task, which also fosters effective motor planning.

resources

A long pencil for each child

how to play

Using their preferred hand, each child picks one pencil up as if to write. With the thumb, index and middle fingers, they rotate the pencil as many times as they can without dropping it.

change the game

🖐 Rotate the pencil whilst raising the arm up and down or moving across from left to right.

🖐 Try different objects to rotate.

🖐 See how fast they can turn the pencil. Count the number of rotations in 15 seconds.

🖐 Use the other hand or use both hands.

🖐 Try a reverse action or with eyes closed.

Peg Patterns

Children re-create their partner's peg pattern, developing in-hand manipulation and the tripod and chuck grip.

resources

Pegboards and pegs for each child

how to play

In pairs and taking turns, one child makes a peg pattern to be copied by their partner.

change the game

🖐 Play peg barrier games: one child tells the other where to place the pegs.

🖐 Develop concepts of symmetry and rotation: make a simple design and ask the children to reproduce the pattern as a mirror image or rotated a quarter turn.

🖐 If no pegboards are available, use coloured golf tees and a polystyrene tile.

🖐 Some children may find handling small pegs hard. Easy Grip™ Pegs will help (see **Useful suppliers and resources** on p. 28).

Threadathon

In this game, children thread items onto a lace as quickly as possible, developing their bilateral integration and hand manipulation abilities.

resources

Threading lace for each child; 12 threadable objects such as beads or cotton reels each (of the same size and shape)

how to play

The children lay out the objects to be threaded in a horizontal line in front of them on a table and hold the lace ready in one hand. On the command 'Go', they thread the objects onto the lace as fast as they can.

change the game

🖐 Add more objects.

🖐 Use different sizes and shapes of object.

🖐 Thread a variety of objects in sequence.

🖐 Thread onto different materials – e.g. pipe cleaner, net curtain wire, pea sticks, a skipping rope.

🖐 Add a timed component – e.g. how many items can they thread in 30 seconds?

Penny Roll

This lively game is great for improving eye–hand co-ordination and movement control.

resources

2p pieces (or play money) – 5 per child; masking tape – mark off part of the table into areas with allotted values as shown

how to play

Play in pairs or small groups standing at a table (or on the floor if there is a hard surface). The children position their coins at the top end of the table. One at a time, they take turns to push their coins gently so they roll down the table to land in one of the sections and gain points. Add up the values at the end of each game.

change the game

- Roll the coins with the non-preferred hand.
- Roll two coins together, one in each hand.
- Explore different objects to roll.
- Add penalty areas.

Party Popper Skittles

See who can knock over the most skittles in this game which promotes isolation of finger movements and finger strength.

resources

Used party poppers, ping-pong ball

how to play

Place the party popper skittles at the opposite end of the table from the children. The children, in pairs, flick the ping-pong ball with their fingers to knock over the skittles.

change the game

🖐 Use Velcro® tabs to stick on numbers to give values to skittles knocked over.

🖐 Use Velcro® tabs to stick on letters that the children are required to knock down.

🖐 Use different fingers, with the thumb, to flick the ball.

🖐 Explore other methods to move the ball – e.g. squeeze empty washing-up-liquid bottles to puff the ball (good for hand strength).

Dice Roll

In-hand manipulation and accurate release are both targeted in this engaging game.

resources

2 dice, pencil and paper to score

how to play

Play in pairs or small groups, sitting at a table. The aim is to reach 50 points. The children in turn roll the dice. Scores are counted only when a double (two identical numbers) is rolled.

change the game

🖐 Change the rules – all doubles except 3s and 6s score 5 points; double 6s are worth 25 points; if a double 3 is rolled, all earlier points are wiped out.

🖐 Roll the dice in the non-preferred hand.

🖐 Roll two dice, one in each hand, at the same time.

🖐 Use a shaker to hold the dice.

Switch It

This fast-paced game is ideally suited for children who need extra practice in precision grips, in-hand manipulation and motor planning.

resources

16 x 2p coins or play money – half the coins are laid out with the 'tails' facing up

how to play

The children play in pairs at a table. They decide who will be 'heads' and who will be 'tails'. On the command 'Go', working as fast as they can in 1 minute, the 'heads' must try to turn as many coins over as they can to ensure that their sides are facing up. In the meantime, the 'tails' must try to turn them back over to make sure that their sides are facing up. At the end of the game, count how many heads/tails are facing up. Keep a score and play several rounds. In this game only one hand may be used to turn the coins over (this is usually the preferred hand).

change the game

🖐 Use the non-preferred hand.

🖐 Use two hands at the same time.

🖐 Increase/decrease the number of coins.

🖐 Increase/decrease the size of the coins.

🖐 Explore other objects to include in the game.

🖐 Mix objects of different sizes and shapes.

🖐 Add a penalty element.

Reel Wind

This straightforward task is great for developing children's ability to use two hands together in a co-ordinated way.

resources

For each child, empty cotton reel, 60 cm string

how to play

Place the reels and string on the table. On the command 'Go', the children pick up their reel in one hand and string in the other. They need to hold one end of the string with the thumb that is holding the reel and wind the string as quickly as they can with the other hand.

change the game

🖐 Increase the length of the string.

🖐 Change the type of string that is used.

🖐 Wind the reel with the other hand.

🖐 Wind the reel with the eyes closed.

🖐 Explore different types and sizes of objects to wind round.

Mouse Tail

A fun way to boost children's finger manipulation skills.

resources

Mouse template (see p. 103) – copy onto card for each child (laminate for durability); string for the tail (hole-punch the template as shown and tie on the string to make the tail)

how to play

The children make knots in their mouse's tail without pulling them too tight. The longer and thicker the string, the easier it is. They swap mice and see if they can undo the knots.

change the game

🖐 Shorten the string or use thinner string.

🖐 See how many knots they can make in a row.

🖐 Explore other types of knots and bows – e.g. practise tying laces, braiding or simple macramé.

🖐 Try tying knots with eyes closed.

🖐 Using a long piece of string, ask the children to tie knots behind their back.

Get a Grip

By picking up a range of small items with tweezers and tongs, children can work on their eye–hand co-ordination, movement control and precision grips.

resources

Variety of tongs and tweezers – e.g. barbecue tongs, salad servers, eyebrow tweezers; things to sort and pick up of different shapes, sizes and weights – e.g. cotton wool balls, small blocks or beads

how to play

The children sit in pairs or small groups at a table. Invite them to sort, pick up and place different objects using a variety of tongs and tweezers.

change the game

♥ Time the children picking up and moving items from one place to another – play not only at the table but move around the room.

♥ Use the non-preferred hand to hold the tweezers/tongs.

♥ Use tweezers/tongs in both hands.

♥ Explore different tools that can pick up objects.

♥ Invite the children to create a device to pick up objects.

Criss Cross Circles

This activity promotes accurate hand positioning and mark making, so it is ideal for children who have difficulty with keeping their letters on the line when writing.

resources

Criss Cross Circles for each child (see p. 104); pencils/markers

how to play

Invite the children to make crosses as fast as they can within the circles. They should be big enough to fit within the larger circle and must not go outside it.

change the game

🖐 See how many Xs can be made in 2 minutes.

🖐 Instead of Xs, make a circle between the inner and the outer circles.

🖐 Put Xs in the small circles.

🖐 Colour in the small circles.

🖐 Make C shapes inside the circles.

🖐 Draw a line weaving in and out of the circles – work from left to right and then top to bottom.

🖐 Try different shapes – Tricky Triangles and All Squares (see pp. 105 and 106).

🖐 For some children there may be too many circles on one page; adapt the worksheet by designing one with fewer on it.

Peg Pass

This game helps refine the tripod, pincer or chuck grip, depending on the size of the peg used.

resources

Pegs, scrunched-up balls of paper, bucket

how to play

Sitting in small groups or pairs, the children use clothes pegs to pick up small pieces of crumpled paper in turn. They drop the paper balls in front of the next child, who then passes them on. The last child drops the ball into a bucket.

change the game

♥ Swap hands to hold the peg.

♥ Make the paper balls bigger/smaller.

♥ Try passing other objects – e.g. marbles.

♥ Use different-size pegs.

♥ Assign points to different objects.

♥ Pass the objects as quickly as possible to see how many objects can be passed in a minute.

Diagonal Dots

This game is designed to boost eye–hand co-ordination and movement control, and can be played competitively.

resources

Diagonal Dots for each child (see page 107), pencils/markers

how to play

The children start with their pencils on the centre mark. On the command 'Go', they put a dot in the top right circle and then in the bottom left circle. They repeat this action to see how many dots they can make in 15 seconds. They do not have to go back to the start position each time.

change the game

🖐 Work from top left to bottom right.

🖐 Work from top left to bottom left.

🖐 Work from top right to bottom right.

🖐 Swap hands.

🖐 Put a pencil in both hands and work from top to bottom for the circles on the appropriate side.

Spot the Dots

Isolation of finger movement, movement control and motor planning are all targeted in this lively game.

resources

Spot the Dots card for each pair (see p. 108)

how to play

The children work in pairs, sitting at a table. Using their preferred hand, child A positions their index finger on the start spot. Child B calls out numbers 1 to 4 randomly. Child A has to spot the dot (i.e. move their finger to the correct dot) before child B calls out the next number.

change the game

🖐 Change spots – give them different numbers, colours, or letters.

🖐 Increase the number of spots.

🖐 Increase the speed at which the numbers are called.

🖐 Use the non-preferred hand.

Jacks

This traditional game is an enjoyable way for children to improve numerous aspects of their fine motor control.

resources

Jacks (5 small pebbles or marbles – or commercial Jacks games), a small ping-pong-sized ball

how to play

In pairs or small groups, the children take turns to scatter the jacks on the ground and then pick up the ball. The first player throws the ball up, picks up a jack with the same hand and tries to catch the ball before it hits the ground. If successful, the jack is then put into the other hand. This is repeated until all the jacks have been picked up. When a player misses the ball, the next player has a try.

change the game

- Scatter the jacks. This time, two jacks must be picked up each time (except the third and final throw, when only one jack is picked up). After that, try to pick up three jacks.
- Change the jacks so they are harder to pick up – e.g. to buttons.
- Use objects that are bigger and easier to pick up, and allow a bounce of the ball for those children who find this difficult.

Build a Tower

There are lots of suggestions for adapting this straightforward activity to make it easier or harder, in order to target and build on children's skills more effectively.

resources

Small cubes/blocks (2.5 cm)

how to play

Sitting or standing, the children build a single tower using as many blocks as they can before it falls down.

change the game

- Use the non-preferred hand.
- Use only one hand – no hands allowed to steady the bricks.
- Build with eyes closed.
- See how high a tower can be built in 30 seconds.
- When the tower is built, get the children to take it down with one hand only.
- Play in pairs and take turns to build the tower.
- Use smaller cubes – try sugar cubes.
- Start with larger blocks, or blocks which connect (e.g. Duplo®), for children who find this hard. Alternatively, start with a larger base to ensure success, or allow the children to use both hands.

Fast Reaction

This game develops effective bilateral integration and can also be used to improve the speed of children's reactions.

resources

Long blunt pencils, enough for half the children

how to play

The children sit in pairs, facing each other. Child A holds up the pencil lengthways between them, at about the height of child B's head. Child B sits with their hand resting in their lap. When child A is ready, they let the pencil drop. Child B has to try to catch the pencil using a clap-type catch (i.e. keeping fingers straight, rather than a grab action). Swap places.

change the game

🖐 Alter the height.

🖐 Drop different objects – e.g. a ruler; see which moves faster/slower.

🖐 Try different orientations.

🖐 Drop two items, one after the other.

🖐 Use larger and slower moving objects for children who find this difficult. Bubbles are a useful substitute for some.

Pick-up Straws

This exciting game enables children to practise precision grips, and also fosters motor planning and movement control skills.

resources

Packet of drinking straws

how to play

Place the straws on a table in a haystack or tent-style pile (coming to a point at the top and spread out at the bottom). In pairs or small groups, the children take turns to pull a straw out of the pile, trying not to move any other straws. If they move any, they miss a turn. Players keep any straws they successfully retrieve. The winner is the player with the most straws.

change the game

♥ Mark the ends of the straws different colours to represent numbers of points.

♥ Explore other games requiring similar skills, such as Tumbling Monkeys, Kerplunk and Jenga.

Trace It

This kinaesthetic game is an excellent way of developing a child's tactile sense and awareness of their own limbs in space (proprioception).

resources

None

how to play

The children sit in pairs, facing each other. Using the index finger on their preferred hand, they place their fingers tip to tip in contact with one another. Child A takes the lead and traces a finger in the air whilst child B follows, keeping their finger in contact with child A's at all times.

change the game

♥ Use the other hand.

♥ Use both hands at the same time.

♥ Play with the eyes closed.

♥ Add another person.

♥ Move to music – alter the tempo.

Pop Up

This energising game promotes isolation of thumb movement as well as the grasp and release mechanism.

resources

None

how to play

The children play in pairs. Child A makes a fist with their preferred hand, tucking the thumb just inside the index finger (the hand position should be with the thumb on top). Child B sits waiting with their hands resting on their lap. On the command 'Go', child A moves their hand around in different directions in front of child B, starting slowly and keeping the thumb tucked in. Child A then flicks up their thumb, which child B has to try to catch using one hand only. Child A must take care not to pull or bend their thumb. After each attempt to catch child A, child B must place their hands back on their lap.

change the game

♥ Increase the speed / alter the speed from fast to slow.

♥ Child A uses two hands.

♥ Child B can use either hand to catch child A.

♥ Try different hand positions – flick thumbs out to the side or down. Alter the positions.

♥ Rather than catching child A using the whole hand, child B has to tag the thumb using different fingers – i.e. tag the thumb with the index finger only.

Catch Me if You Can

This paired activity involves children trying to draw as many crosses as they can – a great way of promoting eye–hand co-ordination and movement control.

resources

Paper, coloured pencils/markers

how to play

Working in pairs and with different-coloured pencils, on the command of 'Go' the children make a series of crosses on the paper. Child A makes a vertical stroke which child B has to complete by making a horizontal stroke. As soon as child A has made their stroke, they quickly move onto their next stroke, being chased by child B. See how many crosses the children can make in a minute.

change the game

🖐 Have different shapes or patterns to complete – e.g. dot the Is, make a V.

🖐 Play in threes and make Z, K or N. Play in fours and make W or M.

🖐 Swap hands to hold the pencil.

🖐 Hold a pencil in both hands.

Flashlight Tag

You can create an eerie nightscape using luminous stars to ensure maximum fun in this stimulating game.

resources

Torch, luminous stars (optional)

how to play

The children watch carefully whilst the adult flashes the torch light on/off. This can be played standing or sitting, flashing the light on a wall or table. The children have to try to catch the light before it disappears by tagging it with their hand.

change the game

♥ Vary the speed at which the light is flashed on/off (depending on age/ability of children).

♥ Vary the height – encourage the children to reach up high and down low.

♥ Work the light across the wall from left to right.

♥ Make stencils to go over the torch to create images on the wall.

Pencil Snatch

A way for children to practise the chuck, tripod and pincer grip, and their eye–hand co-ordination skills.

resources

Long blunt pencils (enough for half the children)

how to play

The children sit in pairs, facing each other. Child A holds the end of the pencil, not tightly, using a chuck grasp (holding it in the tips of all fingers) in their preferred hand and slowly moves it around. Child B sits ready with their hands on their lap and watches where the pencil moves. Child B has to try to steal the pencil using their preferred hand. Child A is only allowed to move it away, rather than grasping it tightly to prevent the theft. Swap places.

change the game

♥ Use the non-preferred hand.

♥ Change the grip: next use the tripod grasp, then the pincer grasp.

♥ Have two pencils moving at the same time. Child B has to try to steal both at the same time.

Mole in the Hole

In this dynamic game, children move their finger to where they think their partner's finger (the 'mole') will appear, practising their eye–hand co-ordination skills.

resources

Photocopy the mole in the hole template (see p. 109) – enough for half the children – onto stiff card and cut out the holes

how to play

The children play in pairs, facing each other. Child A holds the card with one hand and pokes the index finger of the other hand through the holes at random intervals. Child B has to guess which hole the mole will come out of and try to touch it with their finger.

change the game

✋ Add some rules – e.g. a successful guess gains a specific number of points, depending on the hole.

✋ See how many moles can be caught in a minute.

✋ Adapt the card for those children who might find this difficult so that they start, say, with two holes; also make those holes much bigger.

Pendulum

Children can work on different aspects of their fine motor ability depending on which role they adopt within this activity.

resources

A piece of string about the length of a ruler; airflow golf ball (plastic practice golf ball with holes) – tie the ball to the end of the string, creating the pendulum

how to play

The children sit in pairs. Child A dangles the pendulum in their hand, positioning it about eye level and midway between them and child B. Child A slowly swings the pendulum. Child B has to try to catch the pendulum. After a few games the children swap over.

change the game

🖐 Use the non-preferred hand to catch the pendulum.

🖐 Increase the speed of the pendulum movement.

🖐 Move the pendulum in different directions – forwards/backwards or in a circle.

🖐 Use individual fingers rather than the whole hand to stop the pendulum.

🖐 Explore other objects and different lengths of string.

🖐 Swing two pendulums at once and catch with both hands.

🖐 Some children might find this difficult; using larger and heavier objects will be easier for them. Position the pendulum within easier reach of the child and move the pendulum very slowly to begin with.

Flip Toss

This adaptable and lively game can be used to target eye–hand co-ordination and movement planning.

resources

Small objects to flip – e.g. coins, buttons, erasers

how to play

Sitting or standing, the children place an object on the back of their hand. On the command 'Go', they flip their hand up to send the object into the air, whilst quickly turning their hand over to catch it again in the palm of their hand.

change the game

♥ Change the item to be caught.

♥ See how many catches the children can do in 30 seconds, and so on.

♥ Use the other hand.

♥ Place an object on both hands to be caught.

Sliding Pennies

In this activity, children slide coins towards a target to improve eye–hand co-ordination and movement control.

resources

Long smooth surface (floor or table), 'pennies' (5 discs each of about 2p size, which will slide easily – e.g. coins or counters), target (this could be a drink carton or plastic beaker)

how to play

Designate a starting point. From this position, the children – sitting or standing – take turns to slide their pennies and see who can get nearest the target. The winner collects all the counters.

change the game

♥ Increase the distance of the target.

♥ Make the target smaller.

♥ Change the type of 'penny'.

♥ Use the other hand.

♥ Play with the eyes closed.

On Target

This game is particularly suited to improving eye–hand co-ordination as children are required to close one eye and then direct a pencil towards a target.

resources

Pencils/markers, A4 paper

how to play

Place the paper on the table in front of the children. Invite them to make a small circle in the centre of the paper. Holding the pencil in their preferred hand, the children aim their pencil at the target and see if they can repeatedly and accurately use their pencil to make a mark on the target. Starting off with their forearms resting on the table, and keeping their elbows on the table, they bend their arm up at the elbow so the hand is level with the shoulder (as if throwing a dart) and aim. The catch is that they have to close one eye and keep it closed (some children may need to use their other hand to help keep the eyelid down) whilst they are doing this. See how many 'bull's eyes' can be scored.

change the game

- Close the other eye.
- Swap hands to hold the pencil.
- Use a pencil in both hands (use different-coloured pencils to see which one is most accurate).
- Adapt for other games – e.g. Pin the Tail on the Donkey.

Box Clever

This pencil-and-paper activity is surprisingly competitive and addictive as children try to be the one to close up a box and claim it as their own.

resources

Box Clever worksheets (see p. 110), one for each child; pencils/markers

how to play

Invite the children, in pairs, to take turns to draw lines connecting any two dots that are next to one another. The lines must be horizontal or vertical (not diagonal) and each child may draw one line only each turn. As the lines accumulate, each child tries to be the one who can close up a four-dot box by drawing the fourth line. When a child completes a box they can claim it by writing their initial in it. The game is over when all the dots are connected and all the boxes are filled in. The children count the number of boxes with their initials in to find the winner.

change the game

♦ Make different shapes – triangles, rectangles, diamonds.

♦ Use the other hand to hold the pencil.

♦ Use different types of markers.

♦ Play on different surfaces – e.g. put the worksheet on top of sand paper, play with paper pinned to the wall.

♦ Try to complete the fewest boxes rather than the most.

Feely Trails

C Z

U M

V E

Tiddly Wink

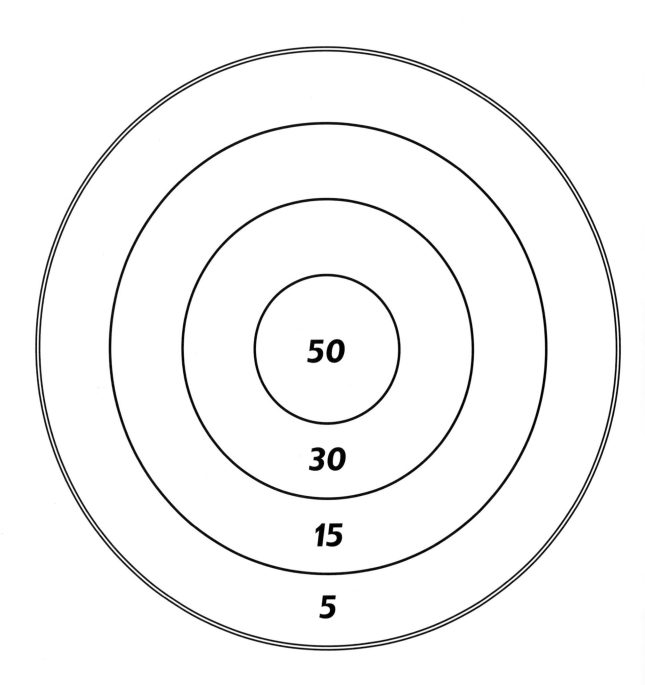

Shape Connect

Use a hole punch to cut holes in the positions shown

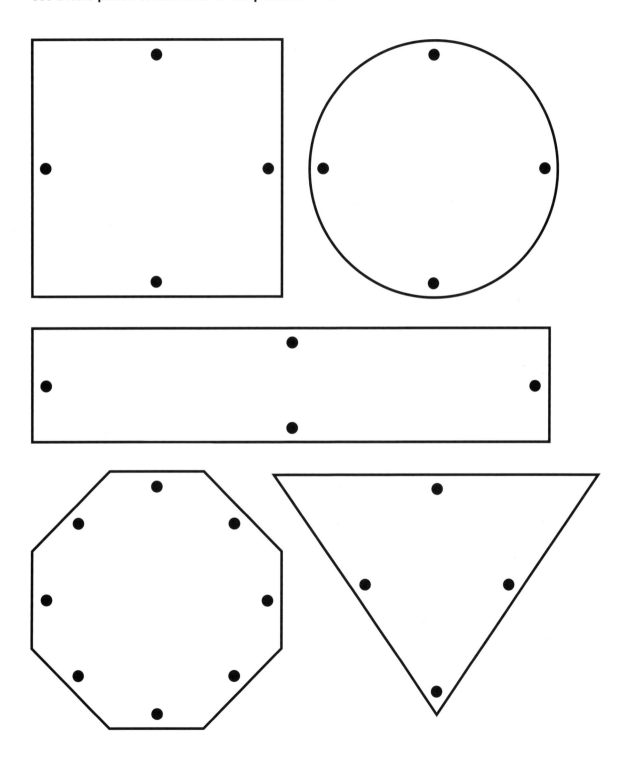

Spinning Top

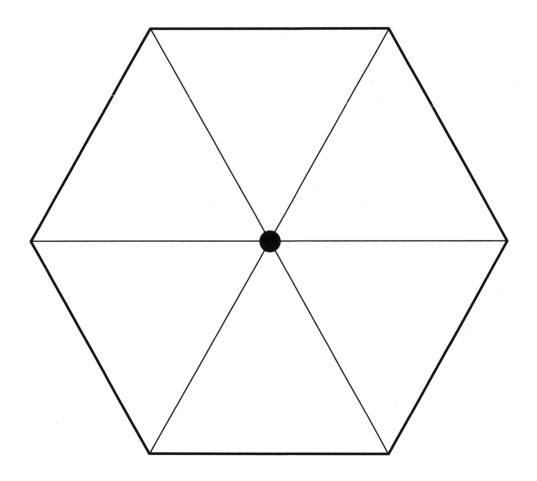

Talking Hands

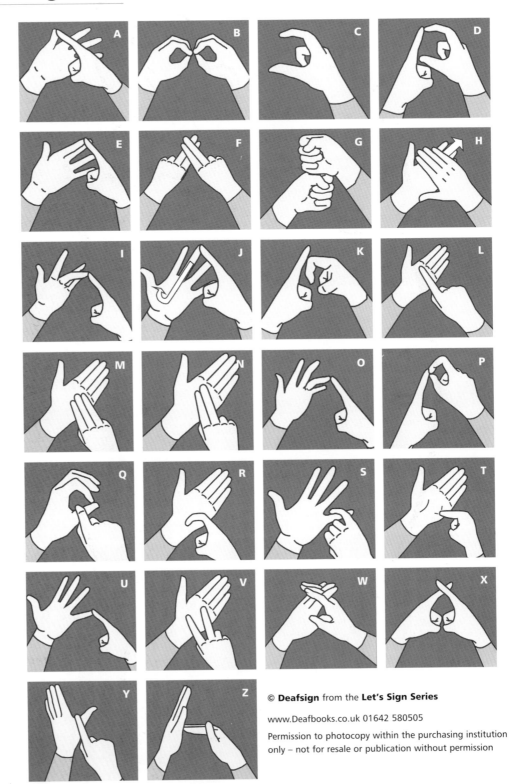

Mouse Tail

Criss Cross Circles

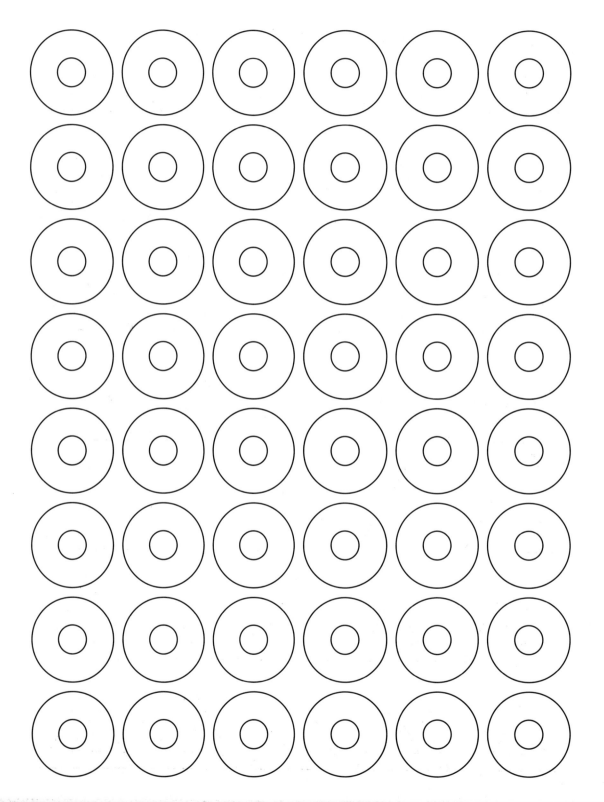

Tricky Triangles

All Squares

Diagonal Dots

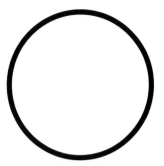
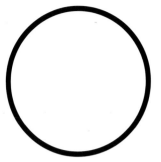

• **Start your pencil here**

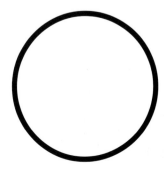
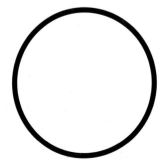

Spot the Dots

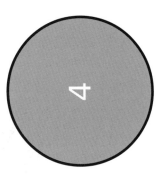

START

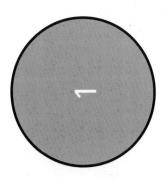

Mole in the Hole

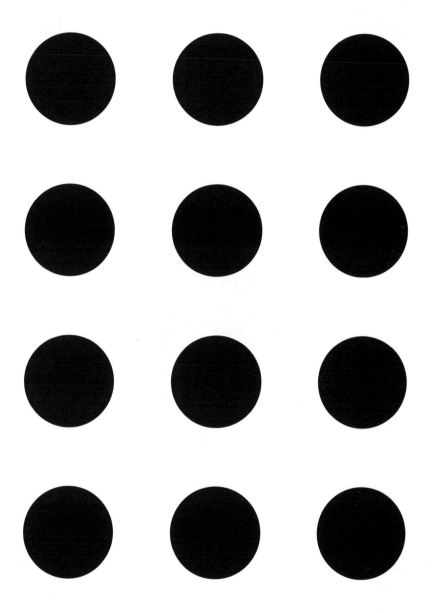

Box Clever